They Saddle Dogs

by Greg Hunt

To Neil

Life's a journey - I think
dogs in cars with their heads
out of windows have the
right idea -
Best
Greg Hunt

Published in 2007 by JERBOA BOOKS

P.O. BOX 333838 Dubai UAE
www.jerboabooks.com
ISBN : 978-9948-431-35-0

رقم إذن الطباعة: 358
التاريخ: 14 March 2007

Cover Design: Will Hill

This book is dedicated to the happy memories of my father

Forgiving does not erase the bitter past. A healed memory is not a deleted memory. Instead, forgiving what we cannot forget creates a new way to remember. We change the memory of our past into a hope for our future.

Lewis B. Smedes

Chapter One

My candle burns at both its ends;
It will not last the night;
But oh, my foes, and oh, my friends --
It gives a lovely light.

Edna St. Vincent Millay

Hedonists don't give a lot of thought to euthanasia. More inclined to reflect on self-gratification, the obsession with filling life leaves little time for the emptying of it. Maybe that is the goal, but everyone has to face death at some point, even if it isn't their own.

The man whose genes I share, who silently encouraged me to be the aspiring pleasure-seeker I am, became the man I would most like to throttle for forcing me to face the realities of mortality. Strangulation, however, was not what he had in mind. Drifting off to Valhalla on a morphine-laced sea of medication was his grandiose ideal of facing man's final frontier. But, as his intake was under scrutiny, he needed help to achieve his desired outcome. This is where I was supposed to come in, as supplier and extremely reluctant administrator.

As usual, my father's timing was impeccable and as usual, he was blameless. Who among us would cast the first stone at a dying man? Well probably me if he weren't thousands of miles to the west. I may not be without sin, but putting me between the horns of this dilemma had 'twisted' written all over it, even for him.

After two years of unadulterated pleasure seeking, interspersed with a little work, I was leaving the Middle East to drive back to my British home base before raising my nose in the air to get a whiff of what should come next in the pursuit of my responsibility-free life.

Unfortunately, for me, the trip of my lifetime would now encapsulate the catch-22 . . . of my lifetime.

It was the morning after a farewell dinner party in my apartment, the last one I would ever have there. My guests had enjoyed themselves. By the look of the room and the pounding in my head so had we all. I thought they'd never leave, but my final table topic thrown into the mix seemed to do the trick. It also forced a realisation upon me.

If you want to get free of tenacious and increasingly drunken dinner guests, as I had that last night, bring up the subject of euthanasia or mercy killing, as practitioners prefer to call it. The police, in the United Kingdom at least, prefer to call it manslaughter.

Mixed with plenty of wine, a debate on premature death is quite remarkable. Even those prepared to talk about it show their colours so evidently that some are dragged away, kicking and screaming, by a partner or, and this was mostly the single ones, become so morose and depressed by the subject that they want to go home and telephone old boyfriends or girlfriends. In single expatriate life, some call this the closet call. No one wants to admit to being that weak and no one wants to discuss the cost of a two-hour, forty-five minute telephone call from the Middle East to London. Made from a hotel room in Oman when you're drunk at 3:00 a.m. is enough to make Bill Gates react as if he'd zipped his fly too early.

One of my dinner guests, Tim, tried to lighten the mood. From his drunken and semi-comatose state, he uttered what could have been a strangely prophetic statement, "Hey Greg, you throw a good dinner party, but I have to say, I want to die in my sleep like my friend Grace .... Not screaming and yelling like the passengers in her car." He laughed; at least it looked like a laugh. He didn't make any noise even when his girlfriend, a petite yet turbulent and uptight Catholic Glaswegian, dragged him back to his apartment.

Should you get any resistance from your dinner guests, and there's always one, ask them what they would do if a parent, sibling or child asked them for help to euthanise themselves. The downside to this highly successful method of clearing your home is learning no help is at hand, from anywhere or anyone, should you ever face such a dilemma. You can talk until you are blue in the face. No one can give you the answer. All you'll have is a face that's blue.

Euthanasia, not to be confused with Fantasia, although I'd rather fantasize, is a highly-charged quandary personally, socially, ethically and down any other 'ally' you can think of. My father, whom normally I never even spoke to unless my sisters made me, had just turned my carefree, whimsical and budding hedonistic life on its head.

I sat looking through the green-tinted mirror glass. It was my barrier from burning sun, scorching heat and a almost-certainly fatal eighteen-floor drop. As I sipped my tea and perched on the arm of the sofa I realised I would miss the view from my apartment. I could see an almost painfully pale blue cloudless sky. It was like that 364 days a year. The Middle East has one day of rain per year on the second Tuesday in February. A slightly darker shade of blue set below the sky was occasionally tipped with the smallest of white horses, possibly albino Shetlands, although this was the Arabian Gulf.

Between my apartment and the sea, I could see a road and a beautiful park where every day countless thousands of gallons of desalinated water irrigated foreign flora in a vainglorious display of oil wealth thinking it could outdo nature. This had been my morning view for the last two years and would be for a few more days.

"Chris, I'm getting conflicting stories about the paperwork we need for our trip, what about you?" That was my question at 9:00 p.m. at the first of many going away parties not held in my apartment. We were less than two weeks away from setting off on our adventure and partying was involved on almost every one of those nights.

Expatriates or Expats are masterful at the art of sending off. They do so much of it. When you are in a country for the money and whatever culture you can absorb or photograph or purchase and have a finite contract, you don't really settle. But, you do become highly adept at meeting new people and then saying goodbye to them. If you have access to alcohol, and little else is available in the way of entertainment, drinking becomes an art form rather than a sideline.

As we finish our night out, in the early hours of our Middle East weekend that begins on a Thursday and ends on Saturday morning, Chris remembers my question. "Hexport playtsh sheem the most shenshible soloo-hic-shun."

Chris was trying to look me in the eye but was instead doing a passable mime of a drooling nodding dog. I, on the other hand, was only able to keep my head upright by using my hands and had lost the ability to speak some time earlier.

We were standing, if you could call it that. The lurch in one direction or another was more than occasional. We stood at the side of the City Centre Building on Hamdan Street in Abu Dhabi. It was where my stunning sea-facing apartment was on the top floor and, from the colour and contrast of the sky, morning would not be too far away.

"I godda gedda gab," said Chris. "Shee ya later," I think he said. It was hard to hear with my hands on the side of my head.

Chris and I ultimately decided that export number plates and the accompanying paperwork was the way we would go with our official documentation. This, hopefully, would get us by car from Abu Dhabi in the United Arab Emirates or UAE to my house in Melbourne, a little village about ten miles south of Cambridge, England or 'YouKay' as it's known to Expats. The export plates were the wrong choice but it meant that we would meet some interesting people along the way.

The day following our drunk, when the bowling ball in my head would allow me, I dropped into my office to pick up some mail. My secretary, Jeeta, had called and left a message to alert me to mail from England. Her weekend would not start until 1:00 p.m. on Thursday. This was not my choice but part of the Dickensian employment regime of our local sponsor.

"Mr Greg, you are having mail from your Mummy and Daddy in England," said the message from Jeeta on my machine.

Jeeta was always so excited for me, and everyone else for that matter, to get mail from their home country. She came from an extended family that had spread from Bombay to the United Arab Emirates to Canada, Australia and beyond. She believed strongly in family and Christianity. She frowned on my life of drunken debauchery and sensibly avoided me when I had a hangover.

Dragging myself into the office, I collapsed into my far-too-large desk chair, which came with my managerial grade. Razwi our 48-year-old tea-boy came in with a large glass of cold water and a cup of strong black coffee.

"Oh, Mr Greg, you are drinking too much last night I think," he said chiding me with an indulgent smile lighting his face. He was one of my favourite people in Abu Dhabi and he 'mothered' me mercilessly.

"Razwi, it's been nearly two years – are you ever going to call me just Greg," I teased him.

Razwi had saved my life so many times with little titbits of information about office politics, reminding me when bigwigs were arriving from out of town but mostly by supplying me with lots of water and coffee. We had become firm friends when I made the equivalent of a faux pas in office politics by entering the tea/mail room to get myself a drink. This was tantamount to passing the port to the right and a few colonial years ago, suicide could be my only way out.

In the tearoom, I found Razwi sobbing, holding a picture of his family. He tried to make out that he wasn't crying but obviously hadn't expected a manager to enter such a lowly establishment as the mailroom. He hadn't seen his wife and children for nearly two years and had just been told that his biennial vacation had been postponed because people like me can't get their own tea and coffee and one of the other tea-boys was going on holiday when he wanted to - bloody ridiculous. I spoke with his manager, made an enemy, facilitated a compromise and made a friend.

Razwi would never call me Greg without the prefix. It was a sign of respect in his reality. I hope I honoured that too.

"You have mail from home, Mr Greg?" It was a question he already knew the answer to; I had few, if any, secrets from him.

"Yes I do, Razwi, and it's not long before I leave for England in my four-wheel drive," I said distractedly as I looked at the larger than usual envelope with my father's name and address on the reverse. This would be a first.

Razwi liked to hang around for a few minutes and ask questions. "Do you not like your job, Mr Greg?" He wanted to know why I was leaving a well-paid seemingly undemanding job because it didn't make sense to him I imagine. My annual salary would have been more than enough for him to retire on.

"The job is fine, Razwi," I said, opening the envelope from my father. "I just need a change of scenery." This made no sense to a person supporting his immediate family, most of his relatives and probably quite a few members of his community too in his home country. All of that on what was probably no more than GBP 150 per month.

He could see I was engrossed in the letter and made to leave the office. "Can I get you anything, Mr Greg, would you like aspirin?"

Looking up, I said, "That would be great," having learned long ago that to say no would bring more and more offers until I said yes to something.

The letter from my father was unexpected. We didn't communicate. Apart from that, I had learned recently from one of my sisters that he was dying from stomach cancer, the condition that took his mother, many years before. One of my reasons for going back to the UK was to tie-up any loose ends between him and me; we hadn't been close for some time, in fact, since around the time my father and mother divorced.

You may think I sound cold or callous as I write this, but my father had had more than his share of terminal illnesses over the years. It was a trait in our family to enjoy poor health for some reason. No one had a cough, they had bronchitis, a headache was a brain tumour and a cut was a laceration.

One of my sisters went with my father to see the oncologist. In our family, that was equivalent to the dead Mafiosi, in an open casket, having pins jabbed in various parts of the anatomy to validate death. My sister's metaphoric pins got no reaction except, as my father refused any medication other than pain management, a prognosis of about twelve months, give or take, for the old man. He really was dying this time and, as he explained in his letter, he wanted me to help by bringing him the sap of a plant that grows freely on the Arabian Peninsula.

Some would say he was heroic and not deserving of my seeming callous indifference. So, I must give a glimpse of the other side of the coin.

Here was a man that never saw his son play one sporting event and there were many. Here was a man who used a leather belt instead of his hand for corporal punishment. Here was a man who used physical and verbal abuse against family, friend and foe. Here was a man so wrapped up in his own world he wasn't able to interact with others unless it was something he wanted to do. Here was a man who had retreated from life, for whatever reason, and had left no forwarding address for the son that idolised him for as long as he could.

Having tried to build bridges in the past I had the uncanny feeling I was entering another of my father's minefields. To my way of thinking to dismiss any member of family offhand would be disgraceful.

Such thoughts would have to be set aside temporarily as there was much to be done and my travelling companion needed my attention.

Chris was exasperated; he'd just spent a long morning at one of the embassies. Our visa for Egypt was ready they had said when he called; he only had to track them down. He'd arranged a morning off work and stood in several queues, then more queues, and more queues and so on.

"It's really not a place to go when you're tired Greg," he said through gritted teeth.

I was consoling him with a cold beer at my apartment. "Did you get the visas in the end?"

He took a long swig of his beer. "Yes, but only by behaving like an arsehole arrogant Brit and I hate being forced to do that."

Another long swig.

"They ran me from pillar to post, the person I spoke to earlier in the week 'wasn't on their seat', they couldn't organise a piss-up in a brewery. I ended up shouting and stomping around the place - bloody hell! Someone had filed them by given name instead of family name. Why didn't I think of that?" He ran out of steam.

"Another beer, Chris?"

"Cheers!" He was calming down, but had a little more rant left in him. "This part of the world can be so frustrating, just when you think you have a handle on it, someone throws a spanner in the works and while we're on tool metaphors the Egyptian Embassy's staff has the collective IQ of a bag of hammers."

Laughing as Chris's humour returned, I said, "We'll be out of here soon enough and just like everyone else we'll probably want to come straight back." Setting out two more beers I added, "It true you know. Many people find it very hard to leave this region. Guaranteed sunshine, no tax, tea-boys and housemaids, no tax, warm blue seas and absolutely no tax - what's not to like?"

As I looked at Chris enjoying his hard-earned beer, a tannoy went off in my head: "YOU HAVE TO TELL HIM WHAT YOU ARE DOING FOR YOUR FATHER!" I thought he might have heard the voice. It was so loud.

Chris, nodding his head and raising his eyebrows, swallowing a mouthful of beer, tossed the passports onto the coffee table without any reference to the loudspeaker announcement and said, "That's the last of the visas then; we're actually going to do this."

I ignored the voice and told Chris about my most recent telephone call with my mother.

Telling my mother about the trip we intended to make was interesting. She always called in the early hours of the morning because she could never remember about the time differences.

"Hi, Mum, it's the early hours of the morning here. Is everything OK?"

"Yes, Greg, dear, I remember your telling me about how the times vary. It's funny that we are in different times and places – it's like one of those science function stories your father used to read . . . are you keeping warm enough?"

"Wha . . ."

As usual, it's pointless to try to correct her; she lives to the beat of a different drum, and in fact, that drum might even be a glockenspiel. The funniest times were when there was an echo on the line from the satellite connection and she would chastise herself for butting into her own telephone conversation; a bit like a budgie with its mirror. My mother is from another era, or species or possibly planet.

When I told her about the drive to the UK, she didn't miss a beat.

"Yes, dear, that will be nice . . . although isn't that rather a long way?" she asked.

"It's about four thousand miles as the crow flies, Mum. I'll be safe in my four-wheel drive," I offered.

"Horrible noisy things and they make a dreadful mess." Fortunately, I knew she was talking about the crows. There's a rhythm to Mum's conversation to which one has to tune oneself.

"Are there good roads from Djibouti?" she enquired as if she were asking the corner shopkeeper for a pack of Rich Tea biscuits.

"Mum, I live in . . ." I still, even to this day, often begin to fall for the 'Mum-isms' and usually pull up out of that nosedive at the last second. You don't need to answer the question anyway. She has asked it and she has already moved on to the next flighty thought that has somehow found its way into the cavernous and eclectic sprawl that is her mind. If ever anyone needs a random thought generator, I know where there is one. You'll get one or two hours of random-ness for the price of a cup of tea and a piece or two of Battenberg cake.

"How's the weather in Cornwall? Is Bill (Mum's third husband) doing any new paintings?" We could have our usual telephone conversation of Mum talking to me and me making all the right noises for the one-sided conversation. Many times, I have put the phone down to go to the bathroom or make another cup of tea only to come back and find her happily chatting away.

Had I sat her down and explained the trip in detail it would still elicit a 'Mum' response.

I had told Mum about Chris, who would be travelling with me, and she thought he sounded like a nice boy – a kiss of death to most of the 'nice boys' mum had identified before. One became a heroin addict, kicked the habit, came out of the closet and went on to be a drug counsellor, one committed suicide due to hideous depressions brought about by voices in his head. "His mother was just the same, you know," was the response from my mother when she heard the news. Yet another of

Mum's 'nice boys' is running his family trucking and scrap metal business now, which is a front for their other more nefarious activities in London, the Home Counties and the Costa del Sol.

What does Chris have in store for later life, I wondered? Maybe this trip together would shed some light. If he were one of Mum's 'nice boys' it was a stone-bonkers certainty he would not be run-of-the-mill. She had a way of picking them. He laughed at the story and said his own mother wrote long letters to him rather than calling. He looked wistful as he talked of his mother. I didn't follow up on that look and he didn't offer.

* * *

If you've ever inhaled deeply through your nose in a sauna, you know what it's like to live in the Middle East. It's almost inconceivable that anything can be that hot, and the smell of burning nose hair is more than a little disconcerting.

Unlike a sauna, you cannot easily wrap a towel around your modesty and exit. Although to see someone dressed that way in a Middle Eastern airport would be reasonably common. You will soon see that the secret of this conundrum needs no towel removing.

First I need to share with you why I'm about to cover 10,000 kilometres in a two-month journey that I could have achieved in seven hours by aeroplane.

The stuff of my schoolboy dreams, I was about to embark on a real-life adventure. Instead of aimlessly stumbling through life, arriving at increasingly disappointing destinations, a glimpse of the extraordinary was on offer. As a clever person once said, 'life is meant to be lived'. Jaded by watching it pass me by, life and I were barely on nodding terms, let alone partners.

At thirty-one, my immature sense of immortality still hadn't left me – well, I had no responsibilities, so why should it? And, in taking this trip now, I was reinforcing that there was, as yet, no accountability for my actions. After completing two years of a three-year employment contract in the Middle East for a British hi-tech company, I was at the end of my attention span as far as work was concerned and was looking forward to moving on.

Chapter One

My father's letter was not something I had expected. I felt a crushing responsibility, well, let's face it; any responsibility was crushing for me at that time. What he was asking me to do looked, at least initially, innocuous. But it was the moral perspective with which I was having the most difficulty. The trouble was I had no one I could talk to about it. I would have the dubious opportunity of being able to form and shape the last words I would say to my father but I didn't want them to be, "here eat this;" or whatever else it was he expected from me. His letter implied no hurry.

I would have plenty of time to think about aiding and abetting euthanising my father. And, the added bonus of possible incarceration for murder in the offing, no pun intended.

His time was running out as time has the inclination to do. It's nothing personal. A flight of seven hours was hardly necessary, particularly as I didn't know how I really felt about the news of his cancer and this latest development. My brain sizzled merely trying to take the concept in. Other than killing my father, which may or may not go down well with other members of the family, I was worried about discovery at a border post. A Middle East jail was not something to contemplate. A Greek or Italian one might be a little more bearable but really, not for my delicate sensibilities.

I definitely needed some time to think and why shouldn't I get some pleasure from the process. My journey would start very soon and I would not, could not, pull out now. My father would appreciate that sentiment, because most of his life had been checking time in-between increasingly brief periods of happiness it seemed to me. Even in discovering life and setting aside the mundane, albeit temporarily, we learn that our own time is finite.

Well, tempus may very well fugit, but I'll be going by road.

I had considered travelling alone at one point but once I'd met Chris and he voiced his commitment to the journey, I was glad to have someone with whom to share it. Having spent the first thirty years of my life telling everyone who would listen that I liked being alone and didn't need anyone, I was leaning towards being more honest with myself. It is not a particularly steep lean at this point but, definitely not perpendicular. Pisans would be happy with such a lean.

Sharing experiences was definitely above keeping everything to myself. Perhaps I could talk to Chris about my dilemma. I had to trust him. Many such stray thoughts entered my head, some even given a saucer of milk and sometimes adopted, others disappeared quite quickly out of the cat flap set squarely in the back door of my mind. No amount of coaxing would bring them back. I would have more of a measure of Chris once we got on the road.

Chris was a Civil Engineer. A lot of them work in the Middle East, not all of them civil. Nevertheless, when you build an entire region from the powdery sand dunes upwards you need people who know what they're doing.

Chris came from a similar background to me, middle-class family, Grammar School; we had some other common ground in music tastes it seemed from other brief conversations. The biggest commonality at this point was the wherewithal and inclination to drive thousands of miles from the Middle East to the UK with no particular agenda or time pressure, a dying parent notwithstanding.

At thirty, Chris was still single, like me, somewhat hedonistic, also like me, but he was also into fashion, labels, and suchlike, whereas I was more into 'that fits and it'll last another year at least'. Differences are what make people appealing. People are what make an adventure.

Surely, I would be able to discuss my thoughts with Chris. The one sticking point about that was . . . what were my thoughts?

The letter from my father was eating away at me so I decided to sit down with a pad and pen and go through the whole thing making notes and trying to get some shape to my predicament. Once I had decided to help him, or not, I could formulate a plan. Time was running out for me too, in a less permanent way, as my residence visa cancellation was already in effect. This allowed me little time to tie up any loose ends in the UAE and leave.

Looking over the text of my father's letter didn't make wonderful reading . . .

Dear Greg,

You may recall your mother and I became members of EXIT, the voluntary euthanasia project out of Scotland, some years ago, I think your mother wanted it more for me than her but let's not go over old divorce testimony just now.

He had a way with words.

You and I don't see eye-to-eye but I know you are not so distant that you would deny a dying man's wish. If the tables were turned, I hope you would have asked me.

Laden words well directed; he knew what he was doing when he wrote them. It was a little disconcerting to know that my father would have helped me kill myself if I had asked him to although a somewhat moot point at this stage of the proceedings.

. . . through a friend of a friend, I have found out that you have a very interesting plant in abundance in your bailiwick and I want you to get some for me. I have enclosed specific preparation and storage instructions. I know your knowledge of chemistry is highly evolved and as you are shortly embarking on your Grand Tour, the two things coincide quite nicely.

Grand Tour was a typical phrase from my father harking back to long-forgotten times when a young man would wander around Europe scratching any itches he may have and learning a thing or two along the way, all prior to settling down, of course.

You will be breaking no rules by bringing me, specifically as there are many variations, the Dogsbane (Rhazya constricta - pictures and detailed notes also included) and to be safe, legally, you should destroy this letter and tell no one of it.

I know what you must be thinking so let me make this burden a little lighter for you. On its own, this plant would not do much, except perhaps cure my increasingly frequent constipation, but treated with other chemicals and added to my present array of pain management medication would be pleasantly fatal – pleasant for me that is, rather than you poor bastards left behind weeping and wailing over my empty godforsaken husk.

He had given this a lot of thought and I should do the same. He continued with his explanation.

They monitor my intake of anything else closely as I am now a suicide risk after mentioning euthanasia to the Quack (my father's derogatory term for a doctor). He's a silly arse but thinks he's fulfilling his Hippocratic Oath.

In signing off, he couldn't help showing his erudition.

As Churchill said, "I am ready to meet my maker, but whether my maker is prepared for the great ordeal of meeting me is another matter."

With love, Dad, seemed more than a little incongruous attached to such a letter.

Well, put yourself in my yellow fluffy bunny slippers. My father was asking me to bring him something that could hasten his demise. If I did it, I'd have to live with that knowledge, and, if I didn't do it, and he, for an extremely unpleasant example, died in excruciating pain, I'd have to live with that; a difficult choice. It was certainly no help in resolving whatever conflict lay between us.

Well, I'd have time to ponder as I drove however many thousand miles to the UK.

A bottle of Glenfiddich, a pack of cigarettes, not much scribbling and much gnashing of teeth produced a decision. I would do as my father asked. I would take the poison he had requested as far as the UK, then along the way I would decide whether I wanted to give it to him or not.

That was the decision that night in any event. I still had two months or so in which to beat myself up over this thing, Oh joy! I was feeling extremely uncharitable towards my father.

I found a patch of the plant in Fujeirah, one of the more northern seven Emirates comprising the United Arab Emirates. It was growing wild and in the exact habitat my father had described. I wondered if the local population had any idea of what was on their doorstep. As if on cue, an old man, who could have been wise, it was difficult to tell, accosted me as I collected armfuls of Dogsbane.

"Shoo hadda?" (What is this?) I said, as he grabbed me by the arm.

He explained in a dialect of Arabic that I couldn't understand too well, whilst miming, that camels die if they eat the stuff I was collecting. His miming would have been funny if I hadn't felt so guilty.

"Maffi mushkela," (no problem) I offered, "You can trust me, I'm a doctor." And there are times, when being flippant in another language, is not a good idea.

"W'allah (bewilderment - difficult to translate)? . . . Tabeeb (a doctor)?" he said, pointing an arthritic index finger at me in astonishment, although why he should be astonished escaped me. He then proceeded to take me by the hand and sit on a rock where he removed one of his sandals to show me the most disgusting case of Athlete's Foot I have ever seen in my short career as a doctor. He waved it in my face. He was very agile for an old man and I wished that he wore more under the robe loosely affixed around his waist.

I looked him in the eye, as I certainly didn't want to look anywhere else; he was so earnest in his foot waving that I had little choice. I took his big toe between my thumb and forefinger as if it were a stinky nappy bound for the garbage. It really was the grossest fungal infection. The skin was red and scaly and his toenails were yellowing . . . sorry, too much detail.

"Mustashfa (hospital) . . . y'allah (go)," I said most emphatically before he showed me anything else. "And stay away from public swimming baths," I shouted over my shoulder as a parting shot. Picking up my pile of Dogsbane I moved away as fast as I could. He was a nice old chap and he would make a colourful surprise witness for the prosecution at the trial for my father's murder.

Chapter Two

The trip was on then. I had my Dogsbane all prepared and sealed in its jar. Time for adventure. Heading into our thirties, statistics would probably prove that it would be the last adventure Chris and I would have and surviving those first twenty-four hours really exposed the flaw in our plan because other than 'go' or 'y'allah' we didn't really have one.

There are many reasons why long trips take a lot of planning, such as, safety. We were reckless in our misunderstanding of that. Looking back, we had done quite well in concocting a recipe for a potential disaster yet more by luck than judgement we survived. It was downhill from there really in an easy, coasting kind of way instead of a nasty, getting worse, ending up in a Betty Ford clinic, kind of way.

Our recipe then was to take two thirty-something expatriate guys and a soupçon of time to get to know each other. Keep them mostly apart during preparation (Chris spent a lot of time engineering a water pipeline in the desert). Allow them to mix a little, stir up and knead in all manner of paperwork and visa applications. Give them enough money; with access to more should taste require it, and sufficient intelligence to be, instinctively, a liability to themselves. Heat all of the ingredients until half-baked and then force through a largish kingdom at the beginning of a long trip to prove the whole recipe.

The result, hopefully, would be quite palatable if not great to look at. Season to taste and serve hot. Like one of those casseroles you get on an aeroplane, they look revolting but taste, surprisingly good.

The focus of our journey, if we were honest, was Egypt, and some particular places in Europe, but we had to get there first. Our euphemistically named intelligence regarding routes through Saudi told us that the pipeline along the Kuwaiti/Iraqi border was "not too dodgy". So it was not enough for me to want to go anywhere near that particular border. I was taking more travel risk than I had ever taken before and made no bones about the fact I had a tight little knot in the pit of my stomach. And, it wasn't due to the Imodium I had taken as a precaution before setting off on our first day.

If I didn't go to jail for Dogsbane smuggling, a rising concern among the international criminally insane community, I had visions of Chris and me being accosted and tied to radiators for years on end, à la Terry Waite flitting into my head on occasion. And, with my luck, it would probably be a radiator that worked all through the summer and then broke down in the winter. You know the kind, they had them at schools in the 60s and 70s, always too hot to leave any part of your anatomy on but you couldn't resist it. And, as yet, I don't have the haemorrhoids that Mrs Termagant, the evil dinner lady, said I would. I'm not complaining, simply making a point.

It was 1991 and Saddam was still in control of Iraq after the coalition-led Gulf War, which was definitely nothing to do with oil. Like the second Gulf War was nothing to do with oil and all to do with W's of mass destruction. George W's instead of weapon W's. Having visited Iraq on business between wars, I can tell you that apart from a war of some kind there probably wasn't much to look forward to in any case with Saddam on his throne. Bleak would adequately describe the country and its future with that murdering bastard in charge.

Talking of bleak . . .

Having finished off a huge amount of alcohol and said goodbye too many times, we were driving through a landscape difficult for others to comprehend without seeing it. This is not the desert of the Sahara. Scrubby plants are abundant but one can tell this is desert because the sun will burn your eyes to look at it, the ubiquitous sand will take the skin from your body and everything has that sun-bleached, washed-out look to it. Nose hairs are scarce due to the intense heat.

From the safety of a car the desert does not seem threatening, but take more than a few steps in and it gets very leery, almost thuggish.

As you fight your own weight in the shifting sand, you get an inkling of what it might be like baking for longer than you had water. Bleached white bones are still a common sight, although they are more likely to be from a carelessly discarded KFC Bargain Box than from a camel or a human.

The Colonel is popular in the Middle East and, funnily enough, people are not necessarily drunk when they eat the stuff. And, just like in the rest of the world, the kids have no idea that KFC stands for Kentucky Fried Chicken. Well, I suppose it could be Kidderminster Football Club, but why would they be selling fried chicken in the Middle East?

We are now quite a way from anywhere but occasionally we pass one of the unexplained phenomena of the Middle East.

"You're our desert expert, Chris," I said, "where do these guys at the side of the road come from? They look like they are supposed to be there, there is no obvious way in which they got there and there is no obvious way in which they will leave."

"Are you talking about the guy who may or may not have a newspaper over his head as a shade and we've seen him about every five to ten miles so far?" asked Chris.

"The very one," said I.

"It's the same guy – he's just a really fast runner and he's got a name you need a calculator to pronounce," he added.

I made a mental note to stop and talk to him at some point, no rush, he appeared regularly. I would also ask him what KFC stood for, as an acronym rather than spiritually or politically.

The first leg of our journey was about 2,000 kilometres, which is quite a few miles too. The vast majority of that we will be in the Kingdom of Saudi Arabia.

Truly, Chris and I had viewed Saudi Arabia as merely something to endure or get through so that we could progress with the rest of our travels. The only Saudis we'd met between us were drunks in Bahrain on the weekend. They would drive over the causeway to drink and whore the weekend away and then go back to their jobs perhaps as school-teachers or government officials and probably condemning the Western devils for their lack of propriety. Neither country can deny it happens.

Incidentally, the border guards on the causeway between Saudi and Bahrain are wise to washer bottles filled with vodka. It must be painful lying across the windscreen to drink the stuff in any event.

"No, no, Abdullah, that's the headlights, pull the windscreen washer lever on the other side. I'm dying of thirst here, but at least our secret drinking place is well lit with the main beam of our headlights."

Would the tonic go in after or would you swig tonic and then squirt the windscreen washers? I could never work that out.

Even in our planning, scant as that was, we never talked about Saudi Arabia that much. As is often the way with these things, it reminded us not to prejudge. It reminded us in a short space of time of the frustrations and pleasures of the Middle East, such as - and it's a good example - the control and restraints on the media.

Saudi is part of a regional phenomenon that has taken censorship of the media to a weird and wonderful level. Magazines are splattered with graffiti-style black marker where any flesh is exposed.

Films such as Nine-and-a-Half-Weeks, although allowed into the region, become nine and a half minutes the editing is so brutal and heavy-handed. Of course, if someone saw such a thing as kissing on TV it may be the reason for pushing some poor individual over the edge and down the slippery slope to such extremes as Christianity. Heaven forbid.

I worry for the poor censors exposed to filth such as bra and bikini advertisements day in and day out; it must be hell. The government has a veritable army of censors and I'm sure they single-handedly keep permanent fibre-tip marker makers in profit.

I have yet to meet a censor but if I did, maybe it would be in London or New York in 'Madame Whiplash's boudoir' being punished for impure thoughts. This, of course, would be akin to one of those seemingly strange Shi'a Muslim rituals but with a lot more leather and studs involved.

Media in the whole region is strange, but in the Kingdom of Saudi Arabia, it reaches the pinnacle of ludicrousness.

The Middle East has much to commend it, as well as much to condemn it. It is relative, of course. Being in at the Wild West stage of a region's development is fascinating and high in potential humour because of the difference from Western culture.

Many in the Arabian Gulf region would have you believe that most of the problems internally are from the West, like drugs and drug culture - that statement is twaddle of course. But 'the West' blames the Arabs for much that is not their fault. It is only fair the West reciprocate.

Drugs are becoming a big problem in the Gulf; in all countries, including Saudi Arabia, although it'll be a good day for snow skiing in Riyadh before they admit to their growing AIDS problem and illegal drug culture. UNICEF has made it one of their priorities in Saudi along with obesity, family health and a few other minor issues.

On the face of it there's not much to commend Saudi Arabia, is there?

Look at their human rights abuse issues and never mind that the country provided fifteen of the nineteen hijackers who toppled the World Trade Center in New York on September 11, 2001. Ah, Saudi Arabia – a constant source of fear and loathing – in a train crash kind of way.

One thing to remember about September 11; it was not about Islam, Muslims, Saudi Arabia or even simply Arabs. It was about some sick and twisted puritanical extremist nutcase, in my opinion, who didn't get enough love as a kid but had enough money to finance a small war. But hey, we all have our crosses to bear, right? We generally don't go around killing thousands of innocents because of our inability to relate to the rest of the world, convince people our way is the right way and because we crave acknowledgement. That day was a devilishly dark day for Arabs the world over. I know many Muslim Arabs who would gladly kill Osama bin Laden if they could get their hands on him.

As a Westerner, it is a little embarrassing that the majority of our tribes think that all Arabs are terrorists; it's a bit like saying everyone from Glasgow is a heroin addict after watching the film Train Spotting.

Arabs, and not only Saudi Arabs, have been demonised for quite some time, more than a millennium. I guess starting a new religion does not really get you in well with the power brokers of the day, 'The Clergy'. You can imagine the Jews at the time Islam was started, can't you. "See! It isn't only us causing trouble; Mohammed went and started a religion. Are you going to persecute him too?"

The name-calling started in the Middle Ages, according to the Anno Domini part of the Gregorian or Christian calendar. Being culturally aware, we need to understand that the Muslim calendar didn't start for 600 years or so after Anno and Domini got together and solved the problem of everyone running out of BC dates. This was the millennium bug of a couple of a couple of thousand years ago. Everyone's tablets of stone were going to crash if someone didn't do something.

"Shit!" shouts Gregorian. "It's one BC; now what do we do? We don't have any bloody dates left, what idiot planned this! Get Ann in here and tell her to bring me a pizza from Dominos – Wait a minute! I have a cunning plan. A plan so cunning you could pin a tail on it and call it an ass."

Thanks to devilishness such as the stories coming back from the Crusades, the Arabs have usually been disliked, mistrusted, or even hated, in some cases - summarily convicted without a trial.

In my racist 1960s and 70s upbringing, those who stole were called 'thieving Arabs' those who did anything less than sanitary were called 'filthy Arabs'. If you were seen to be overly frugal, you may well have been called a 'Jew'. Not relevant to Arabs but Semites all, and of the same region. If we're name-calling, why not get plenty in.

Our parents and grandparents had no idea. Even in the great David Lean epic, Lawrence of Arabia, General Murray describes the Arabs as 'a Nation of sheep-stealers'. It gets lonely in the desert, so 'stealing' sheep was not the only thing on their minds I can tell you. Baa!

The Arabs didn't and don't always think that highly of Westerners either, it should be noted and for good reason. Nevertheless, here we were, Chris and I, leaving a region we had many reasons to like a lot.

The Nissan Pathfinder was humming along and I felt comfortable at the wheel. The tune was monotonous but no worse than listening to Dido. We had coffee and sandwiches, made by my girlfriend, Hannah, and the miles were aptly melting away like an ice cube in chicken noodle soup.

Hannah had been great helping me to get ready; she was going back to the UK to do a Masters degree in environmental law at my alma mater, Southampton University. I thought about talking to her about my legal situation but thought murder and turtle molesting were too disparate.

As Chris and I were getting ready to leave, Hannah took me to one side and said, "Two months or more on the road – that's a long time without sex. If you get the chance to enjoy yourself, do it - I would." I opened my mouth to protest my innocent intentions. She put her finger to my lips and said, "Shh!"

Man! My imagination needs some reining in. That's how it should have happened but we'd had several bust ups over the trip and we agreed that we should call it a day, sad, but true. Hannah and I stayed friends, no, really!

After the initial excitement of actually getting on the road wore off, Chris and I settled into actually thinking about what we were doing and talking about the things coming up. Chris had made copious notes in a book and proceeded to regale me with a few.

Saudi Arabia is often thought of as the homeland of the Arabs, which is not completely correct, but it is accepted wisdom that the first Arabs originated on the Arabian Peninsula and Saudi is definitely the biggest component of that. So far so good.

Saudi Arabia is the home of Islam, the world's second-largest religion by head count and the fastest growing religion in the world. The Prophet Mohammed founded Islam there, and it is the location of the two holy cities of Mecca and Medina. Many millions of Muslims every year visit these cities on a pilgrimage called the Hajj.

And this is where Chris and I started to get the measure of each other.

Chris said, "You probably know this but before they fly or drive to Hajj they shave their bodies of all body hair, wrap themselves in a towel, then go and walk around in circles at the tomb of the prophet and later on throw stones at the devil in the desert . . . among other things."

Before thinking it through or finding out if Chris followed any religion, I blurted out, "Yeah but it's no stranger than not eating pork now that we have refrigerators, having your foreskin cut off at birth for religious reasons or sitting, periodically, in a wooden box to talk about sex, amongst other things, with a guy who isn't allowed to marry, is it?" My voice got louder and more strained as I struggled to finish the sentence in one breath.

Chris had a wicked look in his eye. He said, "But how do you really feel about religion?"

We got to talking a little about Muslims and Islam, which ended up being a staple for us in the coming journey but we immediately agreed that in our limited experience Muslims, per se, are not terrorists, killers or extremists any more than people from . . .

"Belgium," I chip in as I used to have a Belgian girlfriend who said she was Muslim, although not a particularly good one. She had a weakness for BLTs and long lazy days in bed.

"Real Muslims, not to be confused with Real Madrid, are wonderfully warm and friendly people, prone to spontaneous acts of kindness just like real Belgians," I added.

Chris agreed heartily with this statement and said, "Muslims true to their faith are supposed to be warm and friendly people prone to spontaneous acts of kindness."

I added that, "They do not have to have mayonnaise on their fries like the Belgians though."

Chris, ignoring my temporary obsession with Belgians, chimed in with, "According to one of my pipeline construction pals, Islam literally means 'peace' via submission to God, and that Islamic terrorism is therefore an oxymoron."

"I grew up in a place called Oxhey," I tell Chris, sounding like one of my parents. "I don't think I'm a moron though, well, not yet at least," I add. "Oxymoron is a very nice word," I state, and although I don't know Chris that well I know we are going to get on; which is good because I might have hated him. He has rugged good looks, he's educated and he seems to be a decent bloke. We are a dangerous combination though, I fear. I continue with my Belgian tack, exhibiting far more of my mother's genes than I care to acknowledge.

"How many famous Belgians do you know?" I ask. He laughs but sneaks a sideways glance to see if I'm serious. I'm not but he can't tell. "Really," I add. "Apart from Jean-Claude Van Damme, Eddie Merckx and the singing nun . . . who is there?"

Chris is thinking hard but he's good. "So you mean apart from Adolph Sax (the inventor of the saxophone – really), Django Rheinhardt and Toots Thielemans (both fine jazz musicians) who do I know? Well, there's no one really, is there." He smiles and it is then I notice he has a dimple a la Kirk Douglas, but is that a good thing? And never mind that right now, as I realise this is going to be list-making heaven. Boys love to make lists of things and this seems as if the phenomenon extends to Civil Engineers – Hallelujah! We'll be on to movies, beer, sex, the smellier bodily functions and old girlfriends' irritating habits in no time, sorry, Hannah.

We continue our discussion, with Chris referring periodically to his notes. Arabs are then, as best as it can be told, the only inhabitants of the Arabian Peninsula region - ever. They didn't kill anyone, but themselves occasionally, for the right to call it their land. Not many Nations can say that these days. But, sadly, the Arab rarely stands out globally in many areas other than the obvious – yawn! – oil and perhaps their diabolic media image. Dubai is trying hard to change that and dragging the rest of the region with it - slowly.

Desperately trying to drag the conversation back down to my level, I ask Chris, "Have you heard the one about the nun, the priest and the camel travelling across the desert?"

Without missing a beat Chris tells me that, "The camel, even with its hump, has a straight spine."

I have a sneaking suspicion he's not listening to me, but I am listening to him. Well, well, these facts are either going to be hoots of fun or only one of us will make it back to Blighty. My mind wanders - there are plenty of places to hide a body between here and Cambridge, that Happy Gobbler restaurant just outside of Dover on the A2, for example. The service was appalling last time I was there so they'd never notice a body at one of the tables.

I lit two cigarettes and passed one to Chris. I used to do that for my dad when we were on a long journey. The acknowledged and apparent acceptance by my parents that I smoked was a rarity, but not condoned. I was fourteen or fifteen, I believe. Nevertheless, we reached an admirable compromise regarding my smoking, which surprised the hell out of me because I usually had to fight for everything outside of my father's rigid self-imposed laws handed down to him from his father I don't doubt.

We are remarkably loyal to the memory of our parents whether we intend to be or not. My children will undoubtedly back that assertion up over time. My father not having smoked for more than a decade I wondered what he thought about it now. I should give smoking up, I thought, as I blew a long stream of dragon-like smoke from my nostrils. I need to stop dwelling on negatives or it will ruin my adventure.

Chris and I start to discuss some of the wonderfully funny things about the Middle East, such as the emergence of golf as a viable sporting pursuit, which was nothing short of remarkable. Playing in summer required taking salt tablets, wearing whitewash-like sunscreen from head to toe and drinking water like a fish. Unlike a fish, you don't pee copiously; you leak water from pretty much everywhere else, however.

Since the golfing explosion in the Gulf region, many bunkers have been dug and filled. But, not with Arabian sand, it's the wrong sort of sand apparently; the stuff used for bunkers in the many fine golf clubs climbing out of the Arabian dunes comes from Australia. Oh, the shame of it, sand everywhere and it can't be used in what is fast becoming one of the most preferred and lucrative pastimes in the region.

Chris chimes in with, "I know; isn't that truly wonderful. It's like Inuit importing ice for a gin and tonic." I let that mental picture sink in.

We're humming along, and I think I can hear a base line from the air conditioner from time to time, what's sad though is that I find myself joining in.

We're making good time but doing this kind of journey alone would have been a big mistake. Also, try playing I spy on your own; it's dangerous and would be over so quickly – I spy with my little eye something beginning with 'S' . . .

With over one million square miles of Saudi Arabian countryside, more than eight times the size of the United Kingdom in which to get lost, crash or even die in three days it was not much time and we wanted to sightsee a little along the way.

Leaving Abu Dhabi and driving to the Saudi border had been a breeze. For reasons best known, or not as the case may well be, to the Saudi Arabian government, Chris and I could only have a 72-hour transit visa for the kingdom and we had to say we were cousins to get that. Friends or females would definitely been a no-no. Following some bizarre logic, as long as you are in the same male gene pool or thereabouts you may drive in the same car. I have never found a reason for this but, it is the criteria upon which the Saudi Embassy in Abu Dhabi insisted.

Whatever, we were on the road. One of the great things about the Middle East is that if you have momentum rarely does anyone want to get in your way. Arabs are inherent pragmatists, which is probably why they are so good at haggling. We were on our way – day one of the great adventure. The car was eating miles like something that really eats a lot quickly.

Sand, scrub, tarmac. Blue sky, sunshine, no clouds – there wouldn't be any until February. You often forget you have sunglasses on. You don't notice the air conditioning until it goes off and then you crave it, as an alcoholic wants a drink. It's easy to forget what the sun could do to a human in this climate without protection.

I actually got used to the heat quite quickly after coming green to the region and making a few silly mistakes. Mistakes like thinking I could walk to work on a bright and sunny August morning in suit and tie, a journey of, at the very most, a quarter-mile. I may as well have got in a sauna. My first day and I looked like a dishrag by the time I got to the office. I'm hoping everyone had a good-natured chuckle at the newbie; I would have. No one gave me a wedgie or tried to steal my dinner money though, but I put that down to being almost six foot, two hundred pounds with a slightly crooked nose from playing rugby among other things.

The Middle East is a hot place.

The Shamals or hot winds can be so intense they weld contact lenses to eyeballs - even if you don't wear contact lenses – it's that hot.

It takes a new mindset to live in such heat. You know you've been in the Middle East long enough when you open your car window to let warm air in. Travelling without air conditioning for eight months of the year would be unthinkable. Virtually any time of the year you could fry an egg on the pavement, but people would really stare at you and I'm not sure if you'd be able to manage over easy.

The heat is not so bad as long as you respect it, but when you move around or travel any distances, it takes planning. I had a puncture on the hundred and fifty kilometre trip to Dubai in September 1989, and here is a tip learned the hard way. Don't leave wheel nuts in the sun while changing a tyre unless for some strange reason you don't need fingerprints for a while. Sizzle. This is July and we're in Saudi Arabia, which is just as hot as the UAE.

In so many ways 'Saudi Arabia' is its own worst enemy. Nothing like a good over-generalisation to start a paragraph, I always say. The Kingdom of Saudi Arabia has been blessed or cursed, depending on your viewpoint, with all the black stuff underneath it as well as the cradle of one of the most important religions in the world. It has had, and will continue to have, a huge influence on the whole Middle East, but mostly in an incestuous-cousin-you'd-like-to-avoid kind of way rather than in an avuncular sense.

In the brave new millennium, the money is still gushing out of the ground. The country still has an ocean of oil to float upon, but many more citizens too. Having thousands upon thousands of princes in the royal clan, all gainfully employed as heads of various government or administration departments or high-ranking military posts, one can imagine the wage bill for that crowd alone. The cookie jar apparently isn't big enough for everyone's hand these days.

In the early 1980s, Saudi Arabia's per capita income, with a population of seven or eight million, was around US$28,000, nearly matching that of the USA. By the year 2000, with a population ballooning to over 20 million, the per capita income had fallen to around US$7,000. Whilst the growth of the country generated jobs at around 50,000+ per year at that time, in excess of 100,000+ young men are entering the labour force annually according to economic reports.

The Saudi population growth is set to explode even further with female unemployment allegedly running at 70 to 80 per cent; if you recognise women as human beings and not possessions with a lower value than a motor car. Amazingly one still sees millions of expatriate workers in the Kingdom, four or five million of them. Getting rid of expatriate workers would seem like the answer to a prayer that should probably be made more than five times a day, but these are the manual, menial and highly skilled labour and are therefore indispensable, which says a lot about the available working population in itself. This is a big country and needs quite a bit of running. Chris and I simply wanted to dash through it without drama.

The Kingdom of Saudi Arabia is not huge in an Australia, Russia or Canada kind of way, but to drive across the entire country was going to take a fair amount of time so we decided to drive straight to Jeddah stopping only for essentials. Chris and I were taken with the idea of the outdoor art museum, which is in Jeddah, as the only must-see. I wanted to see a cemetery I had heard about, where they used to bury the Christians, but only if we had time.

Jeddah, in one go, was a virtually non-stop journey of about 1,500 miles. One person driving and one person sleeping to achieve such a journey sounds feasible but if you haven't tried it, I can tell you it's not that easy. This is not the M25 London orbital or the New Jersey Turnpike. This is the land depicted in Lawrence of Arabia with some tarmac, scrubby bushes, a few misleading road signs and the occasional white line thrown in.

I meant to tell Chris about the Dogsbane before we got to the UAE border to enter Saudi Arabia but it slipped my mind. If they had bothered to lift the tailgate to look at the luggage I may have remembered, for now the matter wasn't too pressing, too pressing that is as long as someone didn't think we were worth searching for some reason.

Other than a complete reissuing of our travel documents, because the ones we had were useless, thanks to the export plates, an hour or two of standing around and the last opportunity for a while to urinate on Emarati soil, the UAE/Saudi Arabia border was disappointing.

The border guards laughed when we told them we were driving non-stop to Jeddah. They became almost hysterical when we said we were driving to England after that. "Ha ha ha! Mohammed! Ingleezi (pointing to us) ha ha ha! Going to London in car! Ha ha ha! Crazy (shaking his head), crazy Ingleezi."

We thanked Mohammed and his friend Mohamed, retrieved our passports, and drove off. With only the most cursory of glimpses at our luggage, I hadn't really had the opportunity to discuss my jar of Dogsbane sap with anyone. Though it was never far from my thoughts, our shortness of time and external stimuli kept it on the back burner of my mental range. We were now in the Kingdom of Saudi Arabia. I would bring Chris up to speed before we got to the Saudi Arabia/Jordan border. I had to.

Chapter Three

The policeman said, “Salaam alay koom.” (peace be upon you – a common greeting).

We both replied, “Alay koom salaam.” (Peace be upon you too).

We all shook hands through the window of the truck, his nametag read Officer Khalid something, something, something. We didn’t catch the rest. The handshake is customary. Good manners and patience are so important throughout the Arab world but especially with authority figures. Our exchange would be cordial now as we had been polite it would be unthinkable for him to be impolite.

Other than the twelve-year-old boy at the wheel of a 4,500 cc V8 four-wheel-drive at a set of traffic lights who wanted to race around the Riyadh ring road there hadn’t been much to write home about on the part of the journey from the UAE border to beyond Riyadh. We had, however, just been asked to stop as we were preparing for our jump to light speed and on to Jeddah in the blink of an eye and a trail of light.

We had slowed to the side of the road as he flagged us down and approached. Experience with authority of this nature teaches that the first thing to look for is a long beard. Beards generally mean the wearer is more religious and often not as understanding or easygoing as the less than bearded – strange but true.

Some of the beards could be quite long as the owner in some sects were not supposed to cut their facial fungus - ever. The consensus, apparently, is that a beard should be 'fist length' and is supposed to be how one Muslim recognises his Muslim brother. This probably seemed like a good idea some 1400 years ago when Islam was founded, sort of like a Masonic handshake but more visible, but not today, where often a beard is for hiding one's identity and can even provoke mistrust.

Body hair is a personal thing and I mean no insult to anyone but ... some of the beards I have seen should definitely not be allowed out in daylight. Why not? You have every right to ask. Because they were attached to women and even though we're not supposed to look, it's hard not to sometimes.

When you cover something up the natural desire is to want to look and I have seen some extremely hirsute females in my travels. I realise this is probably insensitive of me but I really don't think an 'Epilady' is going to 'cut it' for most of these women either, I'm thinking more along the lines of a hedge trimmer. Brrr, enough of those mental images.

In this case, he had no beard but we did not relax just yet. In my case, my buttocks clenched as I thought of a certain jar that I still hadn't told Chris about. Would he want to look in the back of the Nissan? Shit, I hope not or I am going to have two lots of explaining to do.

It was July, one of the two hottest months of the year in this part of the world. A police officer working on foot, alone, at night, in July was either dedicated, which would be a real rarity and something to fear, or under some form of punishment perhaps. One thing was . . . he wouldn't be a Saudi National. Entry level for Saudi Nationals into the police would come somewhere around Brigadier General. They don't write motoring tickets.

This guy actually looked quite content with his lot and seemed friendly. The lack of a frown from his almost single eyebrow, his dark puppy dog eyes and his ill-fitting uniform that looked like it had been tailored for one of those hugely wrinkled dogs - a Sharpei.

His demeanour meant the rifle on his shoulder didn't even look that scary, but we noticed it because we're British and we're not used to seeing armed police officers that often. In addition, bolt-action rifles are a curiosity these days.

This particular interaction would be a minor delay rather than a pain. Policemen in the Middle East rarely give you attitude. Perhaps they believe, unlike many other police forces in the world, that you catch more flies with honey than you do with vinegar. Perhaps, as many of them are Arabs from poorer countries, earning a pittance, they don't really give a damn. I know what I prefer to believe.

Our peace officer ambled up to the car drinking in everything with the thirsty eyes of a lawman earning US$ 650 per month. That's as far as I can go to make him sound like Eric Estrada from CHiPs. You'll have to screw your eyes up into a squint and pretend from now on.

Officer Khalid was not that interested in us. He had another goal in mind – he needed something with which to write a ticket for the other spider in his web. Not having a pen seems to be a universal problem, as is their acquisition.

In many parts of the Arab world in the early nineties, even 'bics' seemed to be quite a luxury, particularly for government employees. With import bans, trade sanctions and the forward planning of a lemming migration many things are missing from time to time in the not-so-well-run countries in the Middle East. So Chris thought, even before we set off, that we should start collecting biros. He's not simply a dimpled chin, this bloke.

Chris also told me that the French 'bic' pen was originally called 'Bich' after its inventor Marcel Bich but the makers were worried that Americans would call it the 'Bitch' pen. To my mind, it was a stroke of genius to save the bitches. It must have been interesting advertising for the hotels from which we had liberated them.

Officer Khalid continued with, "Where you go?"

Sentence structure from a non-English person is usually amusing in a silly schoolboy sort of way; second only to saying pooh or buttocks at the dinner table perhaps. Unlike schoolboys, these linguistically challenged individuals usually speak a half-dozen other languages too.

I bet few of them can conjugate Latin verbs however; we have to take what little victories we can. Sharpei Diem..

Our friendly officer of the law was now ignoring his other prey, as we were far more interesting. The other chap would have to wait. His car was a Honda held together with tape and string, it was also maroon, dirty and it listed to the driver's side. In Officer Khalid's eyes this clearly put 'Honda man' further down the pecking order. Of course, had a Mercedes S500 pulled up at the same time as us, we would have been relegated to second place. It's good to know one's place in life.

Chris turned the air conditioning off so that we could hear Officer Khalid better. The difference in temperature and humidity was immediate. The Nissan idle revs went up slightly as it wasn't working so hard to cool us down.

"We're going to London," replied Chris, to the 'where you go' question, in quite a matter-of-fact way, which didn't really help Officer Khalid.

"Tch", a slightly rude and negative noise made with teeth and tongue. In this case, it was not meant to be rude, it was impatience, it meant, no, that's not what I meant.

"Where you go?" he said again with more emphasis on the verb. He didn't stop to conjugate.

He asked for our passports and proceeded in looking at mine upside down whilst scrutinising Chris's face. Arabs read from right to left so Western documents can be a little unwieldy if one is not used to them. I felt he was only playing with us now.

Officer Khalid took out his notebook and eyed the bitch Chris was holding with our other documents. Chris saw the look and gave it to him, "tefahdhal" (please – when offering something like a drink, somewhere to sit or the use of one's bitch).

The pen had changed hands and our policeman hadn't understood that we meant we were actually travelling to London by car from Abu Dhabi; not an everyday occurrence I guess. Nothing much mattered now anyway as he had what he really wanted and was probably thinking how he could keep it without asking for it. To ask would have been a loss of face.

Chris felt that we should further explain about our destination and decided to do that in his best Hindlish, which is the mix of Hindi sentence structure and English words that is used and understood all over the Gulf.

A quick example of this would be that the rear of a building, to taxi drivers and almost everyone else is called the 'back side'. English expats say this to one another and have a jolly good laugh about the poor unfortunates who cannot even speak the Queen's English. "You can't get a proper cup of tea here you know," they say. It's not true.

Hindlish is picked up quite quickly if you want to get anywhere by taxi and give or receive directions. If you don't speak Arabic, Hindlish is usually a good get out. I'll let Chris explain . . .

It went something like this and the lack of punctuation is because that is the way it's said: "See car inside we make journey to London, drive to Jeddah, drive to Jordan, ferry to Egypt, and ferry to Greece, make big time driving to London, inshallah (God willing)." It's not as awful as it sounds and you'll have to trust me on that one.

"Insh'allah, insh'allah," Officer Khalid repeated incredulously and in far better Arabic than we will ever manage in our lifetimes. The apostrophe in the middle of the word is a subtle glottal stop that only a true speaker of the language or a person with sinusitis can handle. When you try it as a monoglot, it is probably amusing to Arab speakers in that silly schoolboy kind of way. I say pee, po, belly, bum, drawers to that though.

Inshallah is a wonderful word that means so much and so little at the same time. The literal meaning, God willing, doesn't tell you too much, but in the Arab world, it is used a lot.

Some, non-Muslims usually, will use it as a way to not commit to something. A tradesman who says he'll fix your washing machine by tomorrow 'inshallah' really means you'll be lucky to see him back within the week.

On the other hand, you may have a true Muslim with you who means 'I cannot tell you I will be back tomorrow because only God can say that'. In truth, he wants to be with you tomorrow but as a good Muslim, he knows that is in God's hands. Sadly, everyone uses the word so it tends to be looked on as an excuse more than its truer meaning.

Somewhere in Officer Khalid's mind, however, a light went on. He knew Hindlish well and realisation spread across his face into a smile and a then a laugh.

What he really thought we'd never know, but our new friend, police officer Khalid, who didn't have any laces in his boots and was therefore either, way ahead of the fashion or poorly equipped, said with a huge grin, "You are English!" It wasn't a question. It was a statement, probably on our mental well-being.

"Naam (yes) Ingleesi," offered Chris.

We'd both been practising our Arabic before we left from Abu Dhabi but we were still restricted to words and a few phrases, and swear words of course, which wouldn't really have helped here too much. In my experience, telling anyone you have slept with his mother/camel/sister would have dire consequences.

Officer Khalid's next phrase was incomprehensible to Chris and me but its intention was clear, we were 'Mad dogs and Englishmen' crazy. Then in his best English, he added, "Welcome for my country . . . you are welcome," he said as he put Chris's pen in his breast pocket and patted it possessively. A dark stain showed where the breast pocket met the rest of his tunic highlighting that his bitches had not been treating him too well.

It was the first of many pens we would lose this way and the first 'baksheesh' to ensure smooth passage. A sharing of wealth if you will, which is a most acceptable practice in the Arab world. Baksheesh is not begging, if you have it and someone in need doesn't, you should share. We had about fifty pens dotted around the truck. We had no problems sharing with our friendly Saudi police officer.

As Officer Khalid leaned forward to return our documents, the rifle slung over his shoulder slipped and the barrel pointed into the car straight at me. What should have been a scary experience made me forcibly empty the contents of my linguistically challenged sinuses onto my top lip.

The barrel was jammed to a highly comical degree with cotton wool with a fluffy bit sticking out of the end. This was presumably to keep the sand and dust out but was rather disarming. Officer Khalid didn't pay any attention to my snotty moustache and re-slung his rifle like a young girl repositioning a wayward bra strap.

Officer Khalid returned our passports and said, "Ma'assalama (good-bye)." This had been a worthwhile meeting for him. He had a story to tell back at the precinct, station or mud hut about crazy Englishmen and a pen to brag about. We were minus one pen and minus a ticket - a good result all round. He wouldn't look in the back of the truck. He didn't want us around any longer than necessary in case we asked for our bitch back.

When an exchange between two people, or two countries for that matter, is win-win for both sides, it is easy to believe that the world will turn a little more smoothly. The Kingdom of Saudi Arabia does appear, most of the time, to be at odds with the rest of the world.

Daniel Pipes, a director of the Middle East Forum, a columnist for the New Post and consultant to the US Departments of State and Defence, as he was then, called Saudi Arabia 'the country that is the most different from 'us' in the entire world' as he was interviewed by Ted Koppel on 'on November 8, 2001. The 'us' he is referring to is America, of course.

Pipes also made a telling statement in the same interview when he said; "We have a remarkable history with Saudi Arabia, a history of obsequiousness, of giving them what they want and demanding very little in return." He also said, "Anytime it's anything more than oil for security, we've got problems." Koppel went immediately to commercial.

We had no problems with our Saudi policeman.

"Maassalama," we chorused and eased away from the side of the road. A quick glance behind saw Officer Khalid examining his new writing implement with the pride of the recently promoted.

I loved these things about the Middle East. A grown man, a law enforcer, an authority figure realizing pleasure from something as simple as a pen. His interest now was the other car and his new pen. The other poor person was sure to get a ticket now Officer Khalid had a pen.

We sped off towards Jeddah, a brush with death and morning. I felt myself relax and realised it was the Dogsbane. I would tell him when we get to the hotel.

Feeling more than a little tired, I slept until Chris wanted to be relieved from the necessary boredom of driving non-stop to the western Saudi coast. I was thinking about the next couple of days and the amount of ground we had to cover as I drifted into sleep.

Waking up somewhere between Riyadh and Jeddah about 16 hours or so into our journey from Abu Dhabi I was feeling uneasy and didn't know how long I'd been asleep. It was dark and my shiny, warm, feather-filled lover tried to drag me back into her clutches – I fought her off – shameless hussy that she was.

"Come back to bed and dribble on me some more, I'll make it worth your while."

"Get back; I'm doing manly exploring stuff and trying to tell a story. Get thee behind me, satin."

A pillow or two is a necessity on a trip like this. Travelling long distances requires sleep. Mine was one I had brought originally from England and made me feel secure as well as the practicality of stopping my head from banging against the inside of the truck. I fleetingly recalled how as a child, home from holiday, I would run to my room to smell my pillow because it represented home - safety. Something Chris and I were unconsciously short of at that particular moment.

As I pulled my face from my pillow against the backdrop of oddly comforting road and well-packed truck noises, I became aware that 'something' was not right.

The only light was from the stars outside and the restful green glow from the dashboard. The gentle swaying of the car probably would have looked just like one of those 1950s movies from the front of the car. Except that if you had been standing in front of this one you would have been run down because the driver was asleep.

As has been popular in special effects sections of movies, everything conveniently shifted into slow motion. Now as the slow motion effect tends only to happen so that you can remember scary things and replay them in your head later on I didn't feel too good.

My mouth, dry from a few hours dribbling on my pillow, became drier than a prawn cracker. My entire body shifted straight into high gear. What do I do now?

Had I grabbed for the steering wheel, Chris, my travelling companion and sometime driver, may have fought against me as he was startled awake, so that wasn't a plan. Shouting would do the same I guessed. I gingerly shifted around to face the driver's seat, why I didn't panic I don't know. We were travelling at 70 MPH without a driver. I had to wake him up.

His name as it left my mouth was a gently rising melody in two syllables – Chr-is! This was my best getting-attention–without-startling voice. I hoped. It was quite similar to my mother's ignoring expletives voice. Every nerve and muscle in my body was stretched to the limit for what may happen, which was nothing immediately.

We were still driver-less at speed.

The relative darkness was flying by outside of our world. There was no hard shoulder. The road dropped away steeply by about ten feet off into the desert. The scrub-infested sandy landscape was nothing like the clean, sweeping, dune-covered deserts of the Sahara. It was not pretty and as welcoming to speeding vehicles as flypaper is to flies and about as deadly.

When the journalist, Jackson Bentley, following Lawrence in Lawrence of Arabia asked him what he liked about the desert he said, "It's clean."

Well, it's clean all right because the sand covers everything up. Sand is like water in so many ways, such as it does everything you don't want it to. It gets in footwear or gives too much. In the summer in this part of the world, it's hot enough to melt the soles completely off your shoes.

Walking in the desert saps your strength faster than any other medium I can think of and the heat dries you out in no time. Desiccation is great for preserving coconut but, I would imagine, not a nice way to die. One only has to look at the animals that live in this cauldron to see how harsh an environment it is.

As my main research for this book was watching Lawrence of Arabia countless times perhaps, I should entertain you with a quote about the desert.

Prince Feisal (played by Sir Alec Guinness): No Arab loves the desert. We love water and green trees. There is nothing in the desert, and no man needs nothing.

Until you get used to the desert, there is an eerie lack of smells. Your nose is twitching because it can't smell anything and don't forget everything is going up your nose now because you've singed all the hairs out of it. Then you may get the faint whiff of something. If you go in search of that something, you'll be surprised probably at how far away from you the smell originated.

Getting about in the desert is tough, somewhat akin to wading through a puddle of honey, which of course we've all done, I know I have.

Senses become heightened quite quickly once they are deprived; all except common sense that is. Talking of senses, Chris's were stirring.

Chris's chin rose from his chest probably just as gently as it got there. His drowsy droopy eyes came back to focus. His speech was sticky from sleep a little slurred as he said, "Mmm, I'm tired, j'wanna drive?"

We stopped on the road, both remarkably calm, and got out. My pillow in my right hand, I stood like a frightened child with his teddy bear, my pulse racing.

I was shaken, as was Chris. We looked around at our unkind environment. No roadside assistance out here. Injuries would almost certainly have been serious or even fatal, the car would have rolled more than likely, we had no mobile telephones, it was too soon for that ubiquitous advance, and we were hours from anywhere. Our vulnerability came tightly into focus. The sun would have taken care of anything left come the morning. It was July and shade temperatures were between 115 and 125 degrees Fahrenheit. Shade temperatures would not have applied, however, as there wasn't any for probably a hundred miles in any direction.

The Pathfinder idled calmly waiting for us to climb back aboard. The two-door, four-wheel drive would continue to shine throughout our journey and wear its badges of courage with pride. It was eager to go and totally unfazed by what had almost happened.

"You could have honked your horn or something to tell me he was asleep," I hissed at it.

"I had it covered; we were never in any danger," the Nissan replied.

"I wish I could share in your confidence," I seethed through my teeth.

"Who you talking to?" asked Chris.

"Huh, oh, nothing, I mean no one . . . that was a close call."

The Nissan made cooling, ticking noises, which were oddly reassuring, as it gradually got used to its temporary lack of forward movement. It looked as petulant as a car can look, however.

I took over the driving again so that Chris could finish his nap. We would be in Jeddah soon enough – inshallah!

As we drove to Jeddah, and got closer to our first destination, the road became a highway. We started to see signposts for Mecca. Much as I would have loved to go to see the Holy City, and walk in circles around the tomb of the Prophet Mohammed, because that's what you do, I wouldn't be allowed as a non-Muslim.

Infidels, a catchy name for non-believers of a faith, are not allowed to enter this strictly Muslim-only site. That is unless you were a certain band of elite French military in 1979 removing militants that had taken over the holiest of holies for Muslims. There's always an exception to the rule in everything it seems, they're not usually French exceptions.

Not being French, remotely military or even militant for that matter we looked for alternative signposts to lead us to our goal. We saw a sign, as one tends to do when close to a concentration of religion, but this one was near the road rather than a sighting of the Virgin Mary in a loaf of bread kind of thing.

We discounted the sign anyway as it was more like a cardboard placard a hitchhiker might carry and certainly didn't look big enough to be a real traffic direction. We were wrong but continued down the highway.

Soon, the only turn-offs appeared to be for Mecca and still we drove on. It was our belief we would encounter roadblocks before we actually got into Mecca so we weren't too worried. As we persisted down the three-lane highway equipped with overhead signs, motorway-sized lamp standards, hard shoulder or apron and looking every inch a freeway of sorts, we were taking great care to look all around us and were wondering why we were the only car to be seen. We didn't have to wait long for the punch line; the road ended.

We didn't expect that. No warnings, three lanes of motorway and then no tarmac. This looked like aliens had landed, decided to take the road back to their planet for testing, and never returned it.

Four-wheel traction was the only way ahead from then on if you wanted to go straight ahead. A highway, miles from anywhere, stopped and we were forced to drive into the sand – carefully - so that we could turn around and go back to the small sign we had seen and shouldn't have discounted.

Tracks in the sand confirmed we were not the only ones to make that mistake. Chris and I laughed - what else was there to do.

"I believe the M6 is Britain's longest motorway," Chris interjected.

This situation with the road cut off in its prime is another of the things I love about the Middle East; sometimes the planning is amazing in its foresight; look at Dubai in the UAE as an excellent example, but quite often it is appalling.

In the short-term scheme of things, people changing lanes or taking turnings far too late cause a great many road accidents in the Middle East. Not surprisingly then long-termism is still a delicate budding flower in this part of the world.

Incredibly, in the Middle East, when no plan is available, the powers-that-be will often do anything rather than nothing such as build a motorway and stop, simply stop, for who knows what reason. This apparently is common and historical as there is even an old Arabic saying, which is somewhat appropriate - for lack of horses, they saddle dogs.

The little inconsequential sign we had seen for Jeddah was the correct turning and it wound us around to the main road. The road was steep in places as we made our way from what was apparently high ground. As we rounded one bend, we saw a dead camel at the side of the road. The stench was hideous as we passed the quickly self-inflating body. Nature's clean-up brigade was just getting started.

Killing camels in the Middle East is both dangerous and expensive. Setting aside the death of the poor animal, if you run down a camel and live to tell the tale, you will have to replace the beast. Strangely, they all seem to be pregnant racing camels when speeding vehicles plough them down. Not surprisingly pregnant racing camels are far more expensive than a run-of-the-mill hay munching, one-humper.

It is one of nature's ironies that the ship of the desert, replaced by cars as roads appear through the sand, become one of the worst things you could hit at speed.

A camel has four spindly legs that hold its not inconsequential body conveniently up at windscreen height. The speeding car takes the legs of the camel away and the body mass goes through the windscreen. You wouldn't need Jerry Bruckheimer's 'Crime Scene Investigators' to tell you what killed what, as a ton or so of camel meat at 70 MPH may make a hell of a mess but it is also clearly the reason for death.

Decomposing camels and poor signposts aside, Chris and I made Jeddah at 2 p.m. the day after we set out. It had taken us 22 hours of 'non-stop' driving. Checking into the hotel for a nap before we explored, the little time we had became confused with a sleeping marathon that lasted until the following afternoon – so much for trying to steal time from our Saudi leg by driving all night.

I woke up thinking, if the best-laid plans of mice and men 'aft gang agley', what happens to some of the worst-laid ones? And if I wake up thinking things like that, you can imagine what goes on in my head the rest of the time.

I put the jar of Dogsbane on the dresser in clear view before falling asleep so I had no excuse not to tell Chris about it. It was only plant sap but worrying nevertheless. You don't go to prison for carrying plant sap. In a worst-case scenario, it may be confiscated I assumed. And that is where the cowardly part of my plan sprang forward in my mind. Confiscated Dogsbane could be the answer. Then, at least I had tried. I could honestly tell my father that some border official had taken it from me, hell; Chris was even there to back the story up. There's no prosecution for murder if there's no murder. It was weak but it let me off the hook. The question was how far I should let Chris in on the story. I was tired. I would think about that tomorrow. I would see how the conversation with Chris went.

Chapter Four

I saw his eyes go to the jar of Dogsbane sap but he didn't push it immediately. Even after sleep, I wasn't ready to deal with that part of the trip myself yet. I still didn't have the idea from last night fully formed in my mind.

After several seconds, as breezily as he could Chris asked, "What's in the jar you are taking such good care of?"

"You'll think I'm crazy," I said, "but it is a jar of natural medicine for my father." I was surprised at how easily I lied.

He frowned. "Why didn't you ship it before we left?"

"I wasn't sure about Customs and so on . . . he's in no rush for it anyway."

It wasn't a lie; it wasn't exactly the truth either. But, definitely not a lie. I was going to have to deal with this subject for my own peace of mind and just in case we do run into any problems I should probably talk about it with Chris, I thought. He's a smart cookie so he could already be putting two and two together and making five. He knows my father has stomach cancer. A good question would therefore be 'why isn't he in a hurry'? I would wait until we were less rushed and bring the subject up. I guess it needed to be before we got to the next border in case any awkward questions were asked.

With not enough time to go searching for the Street of the Cemetery of the Foreigners, the place where they used to bury the Christians, we made time to go and see the amazing works of art on the Jeddah Corniche. All too soon we would need to think about driving fairly quickly, with our eyes open, to Aqaba, the Jordanian port on the Red Sea, which we would use as our base for exploring the Hashemite Kingdom.

Jeddah Corniche is extraordinary. After the Maghreb (sunset) prayer (praying occurs five times a day remember) the seafront, or Corniche, when the weather permits, springs into life with Saudi families promenading and dining al fresco. Mouth-watering food smells mix with the abundantly perfumed Saudi men and women as they breeze past.

"Did you know," said Chris, with that here-comes-another-interesting-fact note to his voice, "that Saudi Arabia apparently has the highest per capita fragrance use in the world at more than a quart per year for every man, woman and child?"

"That sounds a little more like consumption rather than smelling nice," I added as we arrived at our destination.

The Corniche, probably Jeddah's biggest attraction, is home to a wealth of art. The open-air sculpture museum is quite incredible, containing creations from artists as renowned as Henry Moore and Joan Miro. One of the joys of the museum is that the public is encouraged to approach and touch great works of art, an enlightened attitude unique in that part of the world and extremely rare in the rest. Try not to touch the art during the height of summer though, as you'll leave your fingerprints behind again. I know that to be a fact because I didn't touch any more after the first one, which, I believe, was a Lipschitz. I'm sure I called it as much as I sucked the ends of my fingers to sooth my smouldering digits.

Opposite the wonderful open-air museum, one of the most famous sights of the city bursts into view every night just before sunset. A huge fountain, one of the highest in the world, according to Chris, explodes out of an incense-burner-shaped spout, hissing skyward against the hazy sinking sun. Showering down in a semi-transparent steamy haze, the whole effect is supposedly symbolic of the importance of both water and incense to Arab culture.

"Perhaps," Chris offered, "it's perfume pouring out of that thing rather than water. It would explain a lot."

"Yeah," I said. My heart wasn't in this. I kept thinking about the Dogsbane and my father. "We'd better get going."

With time so short, we reloaded the Nissan and headed for the Jordanian border. I wrapped the jar in a cloth and stashed it in a safe place in a side panel with the jack. Customs officials would never think of looking in the jack compartment, would they?

We were now heading north. We would be easily far enough away from the Saudi Kuwaiti border to not have to worry about marauding Iraqis left over from the first Gulf War, the war that changed quite a lot in the region, not least the media.

To give you some idea of what the media was up against in 1990, to my recollection, it was at least two days after the Iraqi invasion of Kuwait before it even made the newspapers or radio in the UAE. We were all listening to the crackly, but unfailingly reliable, BBC World Service to find out what was going on. A few days after that announcement, CNN was piped in live through one of the two terrestrial channels and the opening up of the region, from an international media standpoint, began.

The Kuwaitis were not known for the openness of their media, government or anything else for that matter. This is not a reason for invasion of course, but worthy of mention.

As Chris and I drove quickly but sensibly, a bit like how you would want a child to walk if they were holding scissors, we discussed Kuwait and how everything that had happened there in 1991 was about oil. We were both surprised that the coalition forces under the first President Bush hadn't continued to Baghdad, but then it was probably a step too far to actually depose the guy you'd financed and kept in power in for so long.

These days we laugh at the second President Bush's term coalition. At least in 1991 a coalition included more than a handful of Brits, three

Italians, two Polish guys fed up with people making jokes about their country and four Japanese soldiers who were merely excited to be allowed to invade anyone.

We shouldn't forget the rest of 'the coalition of the willing', to be fair, comprising the entire Afghan army (three guys and a starting pistol with no ammunition), bitter rivals Ethiopia and Eritrea because they wanted US support for their border dispute and Uzbekistan because they like to fight with anybody. I like I should add, and five guys named Moh, but, this time there were no 'Mohs' openly in support.

I had an experience in Kuwait just prior to the invasion by Iraq in 1990 and was quite lucky not to end up as part of Saddam's shield of hostages. Many expats living either in Kuwait or visiting had not been so lucky. I told Chriş the story.

Something surrounding the invasion of Kuwait that didn't get any press, international or otherwise, was the four nights of insurgency held before the Iraqi invasion on August 2, 1990. I know of this only because I was caught in the middle of the first one in Kuwait City on Monday July 9, 1990. It is surprising that nothing was reported but let me share with you what a business trip from hell that turned out to be and how I escaped being part of Saddam's shield.

My business agent and friend in Kuwait City, Kamal, asked me to visit in July instead of August as he would be on vacation at home in Lebanon. That telephone call initiated one of the oddest and least believable business trips I ever had in the Gulf.

Can you imagine ever being pleased to see an airport departure lounge that plays the worst lift 'muzak' thinkable, with fluorescent lighting dim enough to be extremely annoying and whose staff, at that time, freely admitted that they might call you for your flight, or they might not. Kuwait City Airport decoration in 1990 was late 1950s industrial depressionist. Nevertheless, I was very pleased to see it a few days later.

Saturday is the first day of the working week for many in the Middle East. Friday is the Muslim Sabbath with Thursday the other day making up the Arab weekend. Having a lie-in or a roast dinner on a Friday is not the same however, and years later Friday is still often called Sunday by Western expats.

The Saturday morning flight from Abu Dhabi got me into Kuwait City in time to see Kamal before the afternoon siesta time between one-ish and four-ish. My driver-cum-salesman in Kuwait, Fadi, was sweet and friendly but about as good at selling as I am at bricklaying and I can't even get Lego bricks to stay together.

"Hello, Mr Greg," said Fadi beaming. Then he continued with his most friendly staccato, "How are you, fine? How is your family, fine? You are fine? Your flight was fine? Alhamdulillah." (All thanks to God).

"Hi, Fadi," I replied, "Yes, everything is fine." Trying to move on from the endless round of greetings but knowing I wouldn't be able to in reality. "How are you, Fadi? Is your family fine? Is everything fine?"

"Alhamdulillah, Mr Greg," said Fadi. With many other people, this could become mechanical, but not Fadi. "You are fine. And, your family is fine, Alhamdulillah."

We'd get into the car and repeat the above at least another two or three times, but I'll spare you.

Later, Kamal and I had lunch and talked about business in general. There were some meetings in the afternoon involving vast quantities of instant coffee sweetened with too much sugar and little cans of condensed milk. If you can't get used to drinking this revolting stuff you won't last long in the Middle East.

Having a driver in Kuwait was necessary as I wasn't allowed to drive with either my UK or UAE licence and hiring a car was prohibitively expensive if you wanted insurance. It fell to Fadi, not being the most commercially gifted, to chauffeur me around.

Being driven in Kuwait was not always a pleasant experience and I spent much of my journeys pumping my right foot to the floor, gripping the passenger handle of Fadi's dilapidated maroon Nissan saloon. I was amazed the car was still running the way he treated it. It had just enough conditioned air to tantalise me into thinking I could stay cool.

The rules of engagement for driving in Kuwait are: if you can get into a space on the road, it was yours, sometimes even that didn't seem to apply. This follows in many Arab and Asian cities so it's a good skill to master, I suppose.

Fadi was quite a devout Muslim who even introduced me to his

Imam on an earlier trip, but that's another story. He reminded me of a young, overweight man who was in need of his mother to look after him. He wore a suit greatly in need of dry cleaning and a few repairs, possibly even letting out at the waist. Although the rolling waistband of his trousers hid the fact that he wasn't wearing a belt to hold them up - if that is a benefit. He was friendly, almost in a childlike way, and I liked him a lot.

After checking into the hotel, I slept for a couple of hours, went to meetings and had dinner with Kamal and his wife in the evening. Relatively early, around 9:00 p.m., I turned in for the night, ordered a wake-up call and breakfast, ready to get going on Sunday morning. I thought about doing some exercise but cut my toenails instead. One shouldn't overdo the exercise while travelling. I read that somewhere.

Sunday went by in a blur of coffee and meetings and in the early evening, I was already ready for bed again.

Sleep eluded me for a while so I watched dreadful 1960s sitcoms on the TV in my room. Satellites only spied on this part of the world and didn't, yet, provide entertainment; well, not for me at least.

My mind was drifting to something important like the chocolate left on my pillow by housekeeping when I realised that a lot of sirens were going off in the city. The view from my window was of the building wall opposite and told me nothing. I couldn't see the street so couldn't see what was going on, which was frustrating as 'rubber-necking' is a key Middle East pastime.

The sirens got louder and I was now becoming intensely curious. This was not your usual policeman late for his supper type noise. This was growing into something far more ominous. I called Reception but wasn't too surprised when they didn't answer. This was Kuwait in 1990, after all. I took the lift to Reception and as the doors opened at the ground floor I was confronted by pandemonium.

It could have been Iraqi soldiers frogmarching hapless guests to their doom but it was nothing so melodramatic. Firemen in breathing apparatus were running through Reception dragging their hoses behind them. The hotel was on fire on the fifth and seventh floors and my room was on the sixth. I had also just taken the lift to the ground floor, which is exactly what I shouldn't have done. Predictably, more people were coming into the hotel than leaving it as this was probably going to be Sunday night's entertainment in the city.

Not troubled by this turn of events, as there was now obviously no danger and I was prepared to let my business clothes sizzle, I interrogated a member of staff nearby.

The fire had spread up some electrical conduit but was under control. I was in no danger in my part of the hotel. That's what the soot smudged, wild-eyed temporary deputy assistant receptionist told me. He did not instil much confidence. What happened with the fire alarms is anyone's guess but they didn't go off in my part of this, supposedly, five-star hotel.

Ever since that little escapade, I really appreciate those little maps on the back of the hotel room door.

Other than my rattled nerves, I was fine. Apart from two fire fighters with smoke inhalation problems, no one was hurt – thankfully. I decided to leave that hotel immediately. I checked out and not surprisingly wasn't charged. I went straight to the Inter-Continental close by. I rang Fadi to tell him what had happened and where he could pick me up. I was ready for a shower and bed.

In the summer in my apartment in Abu Dhabi for a shower, I would turn the hot water heaters off and use the cold-water tap mostly. The cold water came from tanks on the roof that had been sweltering under the blazing sun all day long. It was just right for a pleasantly warm shower. If I needed to cool it down at all, I turned on the hot tap, which had water that had been in an insulated tank and cooled in an air-conditioned apartment all day long. You learn these things quickly.

When you were even in a five-star hotel the same hot and cold water rules usually applied at that time, except for the Kuwait City Inter Continental which as early as 1990 had chillers on their cold water supply, unbeknown to me.

I turned the cold tap on full, left it for a minute as I undressed. A hot and sweaty 14-stone weakling jumped into a stream of ice-cold water. The shock from the cold water was chilling.

"Oh my golly gosh," I said loudly, or words to that effect.

I also slipped as the shock made me try to climb the shower curtain. I wasn't very good at it and fell out of the bath taking the curtain with me and hitting my ribs on the side of the bath as I went down. Ouch.

Winded and with the shower curtain covering my head, as I was being sprinkled with ice-cold water, the hotel room doorbell rang.

"Humph humphing her," was what I heard. Translated and allowing for the heavy fireproof door with its framed little map of all the fire exits on the back of it, it was, "Housekeeping sir."

I couldn't get up as I was in pain, unsure of my mobility and I could not shout out, as my breathing wasn't back to normal after making its forced 'oooof' exhalation moments earlier. I just lay on the bathroom floor until 1.78 seconds after knocking to enquire if anyone was within, the housekeeping person let herself in. Wasn't she the lucky one?

Being a good boy scout I had painkillers in my wash bag as well as the contents of my last hotel bathroom, well, you never know when you may need a shower cap – am I right?

I fell into bed holding my side after taking two horse-tranquiliser-sized pills thinking about what an odd trip this was turning out to be and forgot to order a wake up call or any breakfast.

Monday morning 9:12 a.m. Fadi was late picking me up by almost forty-five minutes. He had been stuck in traffic and I believe wasn't having a good start to his day. He found me still asleep when he called me on the house telephone. I asked if he wouldn't mind waiting half an hour as I had slept in. This was not a popular request but neither of us had much choice; he got on the telephone to reschedule our meetings. My head was fuzzy and on any other day, I would have stayed in bed. I dread to think what pills I had taken but they were only just starting to wear off.

I had a tepid shower without a shower curtain and nursed my bruised ribs. I had a Mars bar and mango juice for breakfast, which probably cost about fifty quid from the mini bar. They were the only things in it I recognised. I hate mango juice.

Monday was a busy day with a long lunch meeting where we all knocked back plenty of fruit punch. Alcohol is not allowed in Kuwait unless you have lots of money; a bottle of Johnnie Walker was about

US$100 per bottle on the black market and even at that price it's still illegal. I used to take Kamal a half bottle hidden in among my smalls when I was feeling brave. Those with bountiful sums of money and good connections however, were never dry.

Meetings that day were a little hurried and uncomfortable. Fadi's driving seemed more erratic than usual. Fadi and I finished the day at around 7:00 p.m. It would soon be time for the airport to listen to the music that would undoubtedly make Mantovani or Kenny G want to puncture their own eardrums.

Having checked out earlier in the day my case was in the boot of Fadi's car, I suggested to him that we cruise the industrial area to see what our competitors were doing. That's where all the competitors' showrooms were at that time. It is typical for shops of a similar nature to be in the same place in the Middle East. In the open markets, or Souks as they are known, it would not be uncommon to have several shops, almost identical, next to each other. In Dubai, most of the computer shops are on a street whose name doesn't matter because everyone calls it Computer Street. It makes comparison-shopping easier in any event.

We hadn't been in the industrial district long when I noticed an inordinate number of people on the streets, people with a purpose judging by their look and gait. Some of them were chanting and waving their arms in that overly theatrical manner usually reserved for newsreel footage.

Great, a demonstration, just what I needed I thought and asked Fadi if we shouldn't cut this short and I would go to the airport. Fadi wasn't listening but was looking a little uneasy as people were now starting to fill the road as well as the walkways.

"What are they shouting, Fadi?" I asked.

"They are saying anti-government things, Mr Greg," said Fadi, showing me a little too much of the whites of his eyes for my liking.

"What sort of anti-government things?" I asked, shifting in my seat, my voice cracking somewhat.

"Very bad ones, Mr Greg, I think you should not be here."

It got worse.

Every time Fadi tried to get out of the area, we were turned back with the road being blocked by military police types and an evermore-scary mob. Armoured cars were closing off the roads; not the usual sleepy police officers one normally saw in Kuwait snoozing in any piece of shade they could find – these guys looked serious.

We ended up getting out on to a piece of waste ground, don't ask me where, but it was right smack in the middle of heavily armed troops, armed with water cannon trucks and other sorts of anti-party poppers.

In all my time in the Middle East, I have never seen trouble that needed any kind of police or military involvement. Regardless of Western opinion, the majority of the Middle East feels like the safest place in the world. This was scary however, and the crowd was building. In the open area with light from surrounding buildings and the headlights of various police and military vehicles, I could see that this was most definitely not the place to be, regardless, or specifically because, of nationality. I remember my mouth being extremely dry.

We got close to a group of policemen who were bearing down on Fadi's car as he came to a halt. For some reason, probably fear, I got out and they immediately saw the predicament of the lone Westerner. They closed around us and they had Fadi and me out of there in no time and on our way to the airport. No explanation, no name taking, simply a need to get back to thinking about hosing down their increasingly unruly mob, I guess.

Fadi explained on the rest of our journey that the slogans were more than anti-government. I had guessed that too. Certain factions within the community had been stirring people up. The hot-blooded Arab Diaspora was on a rampage and they did it for three more Mondays, then the invasion came and everything else was forgotten. Word is that certain demonstrators assisted Saddam Hussein in his invasion.

Fadi and I said our goodbyes, which were a lot shorter than our hellos, with my feeling more than uncharitable towards Kuwait thanks to this trip. Those views would change in another few weeks when the invasion started. My troubles had been miniscule compared with what was soon to come. It was the last time I ever saw Fadi. He got out of Kuwait apparently, I heard later on, and made it back to Lebanon. I never had the chance to thank him. If the crowd had turned on me for any reason, he wouldn't have been safe either. It was good waiting for my flight. I didn't even mind the muzak too much. I didn't realise that Saddam Hussein's troops would be sitting where I was in little more than four weeks though, and that it would be years before I sat in that airport again.

Chris hadn't done a lot travelling in his job so he was interested to hear about the other countries. A natural lull occurred in my talking so I thought now was a good time to talk about the Dogsbane.

"Chris, I want to tell you about the natural medicine stuff for my father," I said.

"It's not poison or drugs or something is it?" he intoned, remarkably calmly I thought considering what he had just asked me. He had been doing mental arithmetic.

"It's nothing illegal and we can't get into trouble for having it," I told him. "I need your word that you will relate this to no one before I tell you any more."

"As long as you're not asking me to break the law, you have it," he said after several long seconds of rumination.

"My father is going to mix it with his medication or something to top himself if the pain gets too bad," I blurted out. "I don't know any more than that, but I do know that the stuff is used in homeopathic remedies around Asia for constipation."

He thought then spoke again. "That must be one hell of a mind-fuck for you," he said, stopping me in my verbal tracks and hitting the proverbial nail on the head. "We shouldn't have any problems at Customs I imagine, but if we do, the stuff is yours, OK?"

"Agreed," I confirmed, "and thanks."

I told Chris about the little old guy while I was collecting the Dogsbane sap. He laughed so hard he blew mucus from his nose. "I haven't hung the flags out for a long time," he said, referring to his runny nose.

It was my turn to laugh. "I haven't heard that phrase for a long time; you're a funny guy."

The road running up the West coast of Saudi Arabia has stunning scenery, from Yanbu through Duba, we made our way toward Jordan in our journey along the Eastern edge of the so-called cradle of humanity.

On the other side of the Hijaz Mountains to our right was the Great Sandy Desert. The day starts and ends around 6:00 in this part of the world and we had run out of light. The roads were good but had no street lamps except in the few built-up areas. We slowed a little but we had to be out of Saudi by morning, according to our reckoning.

We made a couple of stops to drink revolting coffee, smoke and pat ourselves on the back for staying awake and getting as far as we had on our adventure. It was time to take the Dogsbane into the next country. Having been to Egypt several times before, I wasn't worried about being searched, but having been to Egypt several times before neither was I at ease.

Chapter Five

"You are from England? I like Manchester United," said the Saudi Customs official.

He was dressed in traditional dish-dash. He was a Saudi National and his English was extremely good but he was so over-the-top jolly he came across as a caricature. His attitude was disarming in any event. If necessary, I would like Manchester United too.

I have to confess to feeling guilty at any Customs checkpoint even when I don't have three-thousand Marlboro Lights hidden in my socks and underpants. But, as Chris and I had no contraband on us, other than a jar of natural medicine, we expected this encounter to be straightforward, which just goes to show that we had learned absolutely nothing.

Our amusing official talked the international language of football.

"Bobby Charlton." No sentence, no explanation, only a name spoken like a spell being cast. We all held our breath for two seconds. Sir Bobby didn't appear in a puff of smoke so the official got to the point.

"You are going to Israel for drinking and girls, yes?" he said matter-of-factly.

He was casually examining our mass of paperwork, all of which had been useless at the UAE-Saudi border. We both dropped our jaws and then swallowed what little moisture was left in our mouths. Look at yourself in the mirror and do that; it's an extremely visible action. And, at a border post, it makes you look and feel guilty.

"We're going to Egypt," we said, totally bemused, in unison and not a little nervous at this line of questioning.

"You will have a good time in Israel, yes?" He was still looking at our paperwork and flipping pages back and forth.

"N-o-o-o, we're going to Egypt," said Chris as emphatically as he could without pushing the point too hard and with his saliva glands in full working order again. My brain had shifted into noisy mode, meaning I couldn't think of a thing. The next mental stage from that is fight or flight, which would not be pretty at a Saudi border post. I'm guessing.

The official persisted, "They have lovely girls in Israel, yes?" This time he looked at Chris closely.

Neither of them blinked. The pianist stopped playing, I could hear someone's spurs spinning in the distance and a horse whinnied impatiently close by. Fortunately, I was the only one playing out the Sergio Leone movie in my head.

"We don't know. We've never been to Israel," Chris said, staying reasonably calm but alert. Chris had a tiny edge to his voice but he wasn't expecting what came next.

"Maybe you will smoke some hashish, yes?" said our official.

Chris did very well and there was no change of expression on either man's face.

"Ah, no, as we've already said, we-are-going-to-Egypt," said Chris somewhat sarcastically. I sensed he was getting a little agitated. I know that because he rearranged himself while he was talking to the guy. That would be a reasonable sign of agitation, unless he was getting excited of course and that does not bear thinking about. I wanted to break the flow of this conversation. I hate confrontation.

"Perhaps they'll have girls, drinking and hashish in Egypt," I offered. It was a gamble.

Chris shot me a version of a 'what the hell are you doing' look. He also stopped trying to get the green ball in the corner pocket. The official turned to face me. I offered my best 'look at me I think two of my three brain cells may have just collided' look. I had learned this expression many years earlier from the family Labrador. The official's face lit up with a huge grin.

"Ah, ha," said our friend reverting to his magician persona and reshaping his kufiyya (Arab headdress) as he spoke. "You must go to Dahab – there are too many hashish there and the ladies don't wear too much clothes, you will have a nice time." He walked back to his office with our paperwork and passports so it was not over yet.

The gamble paid off, happily, and Chris's expression changed from one of a weeklong constipation to one of deliverance.

While our nameless official went to do whatever one does with paperwork at borders, the workers got to work. We had to take everything out of the car so that the 'sniffer' dog could eat the cheese sandwich Chris had left on the dashboard. His handler thought that was hilarious.

"I didn't think they were supposed to do that," said Chris to no one in particular.

The car was checked thoroughly for loose door panels, and they looked under the vehicle, searching our bags for any of the things that you are not allowed to take out of Saudi Arabia. This confused me because I thought we should have been searched like this on the way in to the country and we weren't.

What was it they were worried we were going to take out of their country? At best we could have got two barrels of oil in the back of the car and only then if we'd had no luggage.

The Dogsbane sat jauntily on top of a pile of clothes and other bits and pieces. If a jar could poke its tongue out, stick its thumbs in its ears, and waggle the rest of its fingers, this one would have done it. It was brazen.

Repacking the truck was a chore but something that we would do many times in the coming weeks. Practice makes perfect. They checked the jack space but said nothing to me about the jar, which would by now, be flipping the finger to anyone near it. If it had fingers, of course.

"Hey, what's wrong with my Dogsbane? Is it not worth looking at? Aren't you at least going to ask me what it is? I'm a dangerous criminal smuggling homeopathic constipation medicine so my father can try and crap himself to death . . . or something."

On the other hand, that probably wouldn't be a good idea for my liberty, my sanity or my standing in the criminal community, where I am naturally, or is that homoeopathically, held in high esteem.

The man with no name returned, he was not interested in our papers from the UAE so we bought more from him. It wasn't a matter of choice. Very soon, we would be carrying a small wooded glade in terms of paper. I looked on the continual buying of more bits of paper as idiot tax.

"OK you can go," the official said, seemingly happy that we eventually fitted in to his pigeonhole. We got ready to leave.

The process took about thirty minutes in total, which was not bad considering I'd queued for longer at Heathrow and much longer at Dover before now.

The entire Middle East officialdom runs on little slips of paper and everything has to have an official stamp on it. In some cases, a literal stamp that you pay one person for and then you have to take to someone else who signs across it, and charges you for the privilege. So, don't complain next time you have to go to the post office; you have it easy. Years later, registering my daughter's birth in 'go ahead' Dubai took me a day and a half and I visited seven separate people in three separate buildings. Almost everyone had his or her handout for some kind of 'stamp', but there's no tax.

As we received our last little slip of paper, which looked as though it had recently been torn from an old Reader's Digest mass mailing envelope, with its official stamp in situ, we had just finished repacking the car. We would not be able to leave Saudi Arabia without this slip of paper.

We seemed to have more stuff in the truck than when we started and I was hoping we hadn't packed the sandwich-eating sniffer dog. It had become rather at home in our truck after its snack. I had the feeling it may have been someone's family pet masquerading as a sniffer dog. In the Middle East, nothing is too much of a surprise.

The slip of paper, with its official stamp, was for the last guard before we went into no man's land and then on into Jordan. The guard lurched from his guardhouse toward us, clearly not happy to be taking bits of paper at two in the morning. He reeked of alcohol and I couldn't help having a little chuckle to myself. Chris noticed it and said, "He's obviously just got back from having a little too much Israel or something."

* * *

The Jordanian border was closed. It would re-open at 8.00 in the morning. Chris and I settled down for our first sleep in the Nissan, he for the first time behind the wheel while it was stationary.

While Chris sleeps, I'll tell you about the first time I had met an Imam or Muslim religious leader (Fadi's). The back streets of Kuwait City would not have been my first choice of venue but hey ho! It was another trip to Kuwait earlier than the one in chapter one, it was a little scary but nevertheless enlightening.

It was getting near to the end of the business day in Kuwait and we still had another meeting to go before Fadi dropped me off and did whatever he did in the evenings.

He was agitated and kept looking at his watch. Trying to be sensitive, I asked if he had to be somewhere. He did. "I have to see my Mullah" (Imam - the Muslim religious figure who is often the leader of prayers at a mosque).

"What time do you have to be there?" I asked.

"Soon," replied Fadi, becoming more agitated.

It would take him 20 to 30 minutes to get me back to my hotel and I didn't know how long then to see his Imam.

I said something without thinking, which is so unlike me as you've probably realised, "Would it be OK if I came with you?"

Fadi's faced changed instantly and a big grin swept from ear to ear. "You would do that?"

"Sure," I said with my mind racing through many possibilities, not all of which were positive. How long I could handle being a blindfolded prisoner of extremists would definitely be a little longer than my span of attention.

Fadi was into the thought of taking me with him, like a religious show and tell, and he'd stopped looking at his watch every few seconds.

Once we'd finished the last meeting, we got into Fadi's car, the whacked-out and abused Nissan Altima, and rocketed off into the back streets of Kuwait City. By the time we arrived, we could have been anywhere. I had certainly had no idea where I was. We could have taken a short cut to the Gaza Strip for all I knew.

We arrived in a small but reasonably affluent middle-class cul-de-sac. I noticed a group of men sitting outside of one of the villas on rugs drinking tea and smoking Shisha (these are sometimes called hookahs or hubbly bubbly pipes).

I noticed what was obviously a headman here. As I approached the rugs laid out on the ground, I noticed that footwear was left to one side. I kicked off my black brogues next to the sandals of the others and hesitated at the side of the gathering. I was unsure of protocol, as were my shoes, which were not mixing well with the other footwear. I'd had these shoes a while, they were typically English, quite formal and not at all enamoured of the desert. They probably wondered what they were doing here.

Fadi went over to his Imam who sported a regal and greying beard, which, as you know, is traditional for religious leaders and scholars. The Imam was introduced by name, but in truth it was so long and spoken so quickly I cannot remember it. I couldn't while I sat next to him so I certainly couldn't now. I find 'sir' works quite well in these situations.

Invited to sit next to him it may have been my imagination but I swear the group closed in a little as I sat down. Fadi sat off to one side with some of his friends. Now I know what sort of thing he was doing in the evening. This was a boy's night out – Kuwait-style. I'm sure if I could have seen my shoes they would have had their laces clasped firmly behind their back and all sixteen eyes would be looking up and around, anywhere but at the other footwear. Brogues are notoriously not good mixers.

The Imam and I exchanged pleasantries in Arabic and then talked of family in English. Did I have any children, for example, were my parents in good health, and then we talked of generalities about the Middle East. This is traditional in all Arabic meetings. A business meeting may last thirty minutes, and if it does, twenty of them will be pleasantries and small talk. Patience really is highly rated, which is why some Western companies and individuals do not do well here. The Imam duly translated my answers for the rest of the gathering. It was going swimmingly. Then came the curve ball.

"Do you know Salman Rushdie?" asked the Imam.

"Run," my brain said before it filled itself with a buzzing noise and tried to pretend it wasn't there. I took a slow sip of my qahwa (Arabic coffee) and gently shook the cup, shaped not unlike an eggcup, as if it were a little inverted bell. This, in polite circles, meant I wanted no more coffee. If I hadn't done that the coffee server, standing behind and off to one side, would have stayed by me and filled my cup until hell froze over. I might have preferred that though than dealing with this new line of conversation.

Having had time to think a little, I replied, "I know of him but I do not know him."

The Imam was expressionless as he said, "Do you know of his book?"

A certain part of my anatomy was definitely clenching more than normal. My throat was dry.

"The Satanic Verses, yes, I have heard of it and read a little of it." I had been in England at the time and, not unsurprisingly, this book had been banned in the Middle East.

He remained expressionless. "What do you think of this book?" he asked after translating for the others. Their replies were muted or if you are a scaredy-cat like me, they were menacing mumbles.

I imagined my shoes had sidled up to the sandals and started talking about the weather. I expect they were also laughing a little too loudly. "I don't really know him that well. I love what you've done with your heels, is it difficult to wear them out like that on the inside?"

"Do you mean what do I think of The Satanic Verses regarding Islam?" I offered. This conversation was not going in the right direction but I was in it and the only way out was through.

My answer brought the Imam alive, "Yes! Yes!" He almost lost control of his enthusiasm but checked it.

"I can imagine how such a book would be considered a grave insult to your religion and I know that passions run high in that regard," I said as I shifted a little. I was not used to sitting cross-legged for any length of time but that was not the only reason for my discomfort.

The evening was warm and this caused a few beads of perspiration to launch themselves on a journey of discovery from my scalp to my shirt collar. A few beads also appeared on my forehead that I mopped from time to time with tissues from the box placed in front of me.

The Imam was sharp as a tack, as I had already gathered, I believe he spotted my discomfort and smiled a benevolent smile. He continued however, "This is a grave insult as you say, what would you think if we criticised your British royal family this way?"

It was my time to laugh and release a little tension. "The Press in England do that every day," I said. "Some characters, like Prince Charles, come in for an inordinate amount of ridicule by the press (a lot of it quite justified I thought to myself). Having a Free Press means that you are allowed to say what you wish as long as it's not illegal, such as inciting people to riot, telling lies about someone, or giving away state secrets, that sort of thing."

"But Salman Rushie has lied about Islam," said the Imam incredulously and was obviously trying to build a case. The ones in the group who could not understand what we were saying must have been totally lost by now, as the translating had ceased.

The Satanic Verses had been a huge topic of conversation in the Middle East. I had been party to many conversations between Muslims, Christians, Hindus and those, like me who sat on the spiritual fence - or was that in the spiritual abyss.

Remembering some of the conversations and the little I'd read on what some thought was Rushdie trying to sensationalise to sell books. I said, "Can you prove that Rushdie is lying as he talks of good and evil more than anything else, I believe. He is giving his opinion and opinion is fair game in a free society . . . if my memory is correct, one of my

Muslim friends says the title of the book comes from the theological discussion regarding whether it is possible to accept that satanic verses could somehow be insinuated into the prophet's message from God?"

My brain stopped buzzing long enough to congratulate the semantic part of itself, which it obviously had no control over. The Imam raised one eyebrow Roger Moore style and for once, in a stressful situation, my brain had not totally failed me. I didn't have to shout, "Ooh! Look over there!" And then run like hell.

The Satanic Verses was, it would appear, as I still haven't read it all, a well-written book. But if sensationalism was what Rushdie was after, I think he got a lot more than he bargained for. He is under threat of death to this day and as the person who issued the fatwah (a legal ruling issued by an Islamic scholar and in this case a death sentence) is dead, I believe, it will stand until Rushdie is dead whether that be naturally or not.

Everyone was trying to get hold of copies of Rushdie's book to put on their coffee tables to impress visitors, but I fear it was a little like *A Brief History Of Time*, more often used for stopping coffee tables from wobbling rather than being read.

"We will write a book about Salman Rushdie," said the Imam after some thought.

"That would not be a good idea if you are intending to libel him as he would be protected by British and international law," I said sounding as apologetic as possible and my brain was wishing I would keep my mouth shut. My brain never took responsibility for anything.

"This is wrong that such a man should be protected by your laws," said the Imam sadly.

"He's not only protected by our laws since the serious death threats against him, he has also been protected by the Special Branch, one of our elite police agencies," I told him. And, I hope they remember I said that about them if they pull me up for laxative smuggling or conspiracy to commit murder in Dover.

"Incredible that you should protect him so well," said the Imam shaking his head.

"If it helps, sir," I offered, "Britain would give you the same protection should you write your opinion about the Bible, the Pope, Salman Rushdie or Margaret Thatcher. If you wrote something about Margaret Thatcher some would carry you on their shoulders."

"Thatcher is strong, not like a woman at all," he said with a clenched fist. I imagined the questioning of Mrs Thatcher's sexuality was a back-handed compliment. I relaxed a little – we were back on an even keel now.

The conversation died down and for the next few minutes the Imam explained what had been said. Every now and then, they would look at me. They ran through the whole gamut of facial expressions and I was hoping they would still let me leave at some point.

The Imam ended by indicating me and the one of the only words I recognised, as usual, was 'Ingleezi'. The 'Audience' was ending. I saw Fadi getting ready to get up. I was hoping against hope I had done the right thing and getting out of Dodge seemed a smart idea. I turned to the Imam. "Sir if I may take your leave I have had a long day and wish to go to my hotel."

"We must not keep you," he said with a wry smile and a glint in his eye.

We stood together and it was then I saw the assault rifle lying half covered on the ground behind him. I averted my gaze too slowly. He saw and said, "I have enemies." I didn't pursue that statement but clenched my buttocks to the point where I wondered if I would be able to walk without consuming my trousers or at the very least mincing embarrassingly.

He offered his hand and totally relaxed me (and my buttocks) with what he said, "You are an honest man."

With my buttocks still getting used to their new relaxed state I said, "Shukran (thank you), maassalma." I realised that I had been grinding my teeth hard too as my jaw ached.

Fadi explained that the Imam was one of the most outspoken against the government of Kuwait and that he had a large following in the city. He said that there had been threats against his life. I wondered if I would have gone had I known, probably not, but I'm glad I did. As we left and drove out of the cul-de-sac, I caught a glimpse of them back to sitting and talking. I guess a revolution has to start somewhere. I eased myself back into the passenger seat, tried to relax and realised my heart had been trying to beat its way out of my chest and my mouth was drier than dust.

Isn't it funny how badly you crave a beer when you know you can't have one?

Back at the Jordanian border, the sun is shining in through the Nissan's windows – a Middle Eastern alarm clock. If the sun doesn't wake you, the heat surely will.

I awoke as Chris opened his door to get out of the Nissan. "Something died in here," said Chris. "And boy, do you snore."

"Good morning to you too, dragon breath," I countered. "Let's really try and not sleep in the truck any more than we really have to, eh?" I tried straightening the kinks in my body, struggling upright.

"You'll get no argument from me in that regard. I will petition the king for a border hotel the moment we run into him in Amman," said Chris with a flourish and deep bow.

"Time to 'do' Jordan," I said, still stretching the crumples of a night in a car seat from my body. We were the only ones at the border post apart from Jordan's front line defences against Saudi invasion.

The Jordanian border guard was preparing his breakfast of bread, cheese and tea. Without a thought, he offered an equal share of what he had to us. We were not green enough to refuse out of our Western idea of good manners. To refuse would have been bordering on an insult. It was a different border we were looking to cross.

There are few places in the world where this level of consideration for travellers is even thought about let alone being part of the way of life as it is in the Arab world. The pleasantries of this world can be embarrassing to the Western races sometimes because we used to be like that, considerate and polite, but rarely are these days.

The border guard was truly sad to break his bad news to us, which is another trait of the Arabs and often I have come across a person who would rather tell you something completely wrong rather than tell you bad news – more saddling dogs for want of a horse. It's only disturbing for a while then it is actually quite pleasant; akin to peeing in a wetsuit on a cold day's waterskiing.

"You do not have the right papers for Jordan," he said with rather better English than we could have hoped. At least if his English had been bad we could have clung to the hope that he was confused.

"You need a trip ticket from your setting off destination to your final ending," he explained. His sentence construction missed the target somewhat but not the meaning.

The bloody paperwork and the bloody export plates on the truck again. No mention of all this nonsense had been made at the Jordanian embassy and our advice had been not to get a trip ticket, whatever that was, from others we had spoken with. This was going to dog us until Europe now, we were sure of that. Still we had personal visas and getting them from the Jordanian embassy had been interesting to say the least.

On the day I submitted the visa applications, Chris had been in the desert looking at a hole in the ground or something, and couldn't come with me. Unbeknown to me at the time, he had forgotten to sign his visa application.

Entering the embassy, the crowd before me parted rather as I imagine the Red Sea would have, had I been Moses. I was ushered to the front of the queue; this was the first time this had ever happened to me and I looked behind me first to see if someone important had entered the room.

My explanation for this parting of the waves of humanity was because I was the only Westerner in the room. I had no other explanation. It felt as if I'd walked into a meeting where everyone was talking about me.

"Look out, lads, here he is . . . pretend you're getting a visa too, but let him go to the front of the line. He'll think it's because he's white – you know what these Brits are like."

Maybe if I'd looked closely I would have seen all the people who didn't like me from the previous thirty years, nah, that's too freaky, right. I'll have to talk to my therapist about that one.

Queues in the Middle East are actually of interest to British people because firstly, you don't line up in a crocodile and secondly, because the British are the best at queuing in the world. We have to be the best at something; with our laissez faire attitude toward games, we're hardly going to make any more noise in the world of sport. So, queuing it is then.

Queues in the Middle East are one deep and forty-eight people wide, even when there are only forty-seven people in the room. They contain an element of every man for himself. I say 'man' because either there would be a separate queue for women or she probably wouldn't be there at all. As Bruce Hornsby said, "That's just the way it is, some things may never change."

If you queue in a bank or anywhere else in the Arab world and a woman comes in, and no special line is allotted for her, she will walk to the front without batting an eyelid. All the coughing in the world won't make her go to the back either. I tried it when I first got to that part of the world and ended up with a sore throat. Tutting, huffing and rolling your eyes doesn't help either because I've tried that too. We British have that awful belief that there is only one way to queue and it's the right way. We're obviously wrong.

The odds were in my favour in the Jordanian embassy. I even signed Chris's visa application at the suggestion of the embassy official looking after me.

"This is not me," I naively said, indicating Chris's passport.

"Maffi mushkela" (no problem), he said. Perhaps he didn't understand who knows, and any way, maffi mushkela!

As I finished signing I told him we were driving to London via Jordan and he laughed, "Yes sir, very good sir," he said. He wasn't listening. I guess I should have noticed that. The visas were processed but there was no mention of driving. To that end, Chris and I were welcome in Jordan but the car was not.

Chapter Six

"We could hire a car," offered Chris.

"You saw the prices. It's hideously expensive and you and I would want insurance, which puts it out of the realm of our budget," I countered. I didn't want to be negative but we had to keep some reality to our spending. "We could go by foot."

"Yes, we could . . . oh look there's one of those little flying pink things with a curly tail," he said sarcastically. Neither of us would have walked, or bussed or even taken any other mode of transport that didn't involve driving. We were both spoilt brats who had grown up into bigger spoilt brats. When our families weren't spoiling us, we were spoiling ourselves. At least we were honest about it.

"I don't fancy leaving the car anyway," I said.

"Nor me," said Chris. We both laughed. Who were we kidding, well, not ourselves?

"It looks like we'll have to leave Jordan for another time," I said somewhat dejectedly.

"I don't see another choice," said Chris.

The change in plans was a real blow. It had been our intention to stay two or three weeks in Jordan. It is a country rich in history but particularly in that, East meets West kind of way. Jordan is not just the mystical city of Petra it is a hugely important country to Christians and Muslims for many reasons. Chris had gone to work on research before we even got to Jordan. He gave me the highlights.

John the Baptist was a good place to start. He was busy in Jordan in a place called Bethany, for reference see the closest copy of a Bible – John 1:28. It is also believed to be the site of Jesus's baptism, although with the religion based around Him and His Dad I'd always wondered why he needed to be baptised. It seemed a bit like Bill Gates buying a copy of Windows.

I wonder if Windows has more users than Christianity these days. Just a thought.

Don't confuse John the Baptist's Bethany with the Bethany east of the river Jordan, the hometown of Lazarus; many people do apparently. The prophet Elijah, or Mar Elias for Muslims, ascended heaven from this Bethany in a whirlwind on a chariot of fire, this was only after parting waters and walking across to the other side with his anointed successor the Prophet Elisha. Parting waters or splitty d'leau as it was often known was the de rigueur party piece for any self-respecting prophet in those days. You can get the full details from 2 Kings 2; 5 – 14 in your handy dandy Bible.

Byzantine writers in the fifth and sixth centuries did a good job in building the country up as a tourist magnet for later years. The country is overrun with great stuff to go and stand in, on or near and have your picture taken. For example, there's the Dead Sea, Umm Al Rassas, Amman, Umm Qais, the Zerqa River, the King's Highway, the spring of Moses (I thought about going for the cheap laugh here and avoided it), Kerak, Wadi Arabah and Lot's Sanctuary (mm salty!). Need I go on? I hope not, as I'd only heard of the Dead Sea.

Nevertheless, this is also a very important country to Muslims.

A large number of the Prophet Mohammed's companions were martyred and buried in Jordan, for Jordan was the first territory outside the Arabian Peninsula to which Islam spread, it was also the first point of contact between Islam and the non-Arab world.

The three most important historical sites to Islam in Jordan are the Battle of Mutah and the site of two battles at Yarmouk and the Battle of Fahl.

There's something about battle sites. Unless there's a battle going on, they're not that interesting. I've been to Hastings, Little Big Horn, and Culloden - bugger all going on. I'd rather wax my back. The sites of battles I've never even heard of, well, not a big miss for me. It might not mean anything to me but then as a heathen, I'm used to things not meaning much to me. My father taught me well: don't invest in anything emotionally and then it can't bite you in the arse later on.

Chris is telling me that, "Jordan is also apparently the site of the famous childhood encounter of the prophet Mohammed with the Monk Bhira and the later encounter with the Monk Nestor at the site of Mayfa'ah also known as Umm al Rassas."

"Chris, stop telling me this stuff. We're not going to see any of it anyway and you are starting to wind me up," I said.

"OK but just let me tell you this one," he said enthusiastically and reading from his notes. "Mysterious as its name suggests, the cave of the Seven Sleepers, which may or may not have relevance to Snow White, is unique among the religious sites in Jordan." He looked up to see if I was still being petulant. "Its mystical story is supported by a chapter in the Koran and by the parallel Christian legend of Ephesus."

This started to make me think, which is dangerous at the best of times, but while the grey matter is stirring of its own volition, I tend to let it have free rein. Chris carried on talking but my brain, which I often think of as a separate entity anyway, had wandered.

Assuming all the Islamic, Hebrew and Christian shenanigans of hundreds of years ago in this region are true, and I could go either way on this, I wonder what Jesus Christ or the Prophet Mohammed would make of the conflict in this region now. Now there's a book to write. It would have highly charged dialogue.

"Hey, Jesus! What is it with these people? We give them a few really simple rules to follow to make their lives pleasant and they screw it up."

"Oy vey! I know, Moh, if you listen to their nonsense you'd think Satan insinuated some verses into those rules you gave them to live by."

The only ones smiling are the devil and his disciples who may not be who we think they are.

From anything I have read of this region's religions, and try saying that with a mouth full of marbles, I believe both of these characters, so fundamental to the respective faith in the world, would be appalled at the atrocities conducted in their names and in the names of the respective religions. It is merely an opinion. And, as my grandfather always used to say, opinions are like rear ends – everybody has one. He didn't say rear ends but for an old gentleman he could be so crass at times.

In any event, Chris and I weren't to stand in, on or near any of this wonderful history and religious significance. I made a mental note to come back one day with the correct paperwork.

Chris telling me that there is no mention in the Bible of Adam and Eve ever eating an apple shook my reverie. Had he been reading my biblical thoughts?

The official Jordanian worry regarding our stay in the Hashemite Kingdom was that we would try to sell the truck, thus avoiding taxes, and no amount of explaining that we were on our way to London by said car would sway our pleasant Jordanian official.

Ma'assalma. We eventually went straight to the ferry port in Aqaba in a police escorted convoy along with some trucks carrying homeopathic laxatives from Saudi Arabia to Jordan and the police car leading the way held our passports. We made the port disappointed but eager to get on regardless. We sang.

"Always look on the bright side of life . . ."

We didn't really sing, but we could have.

Aqaba's changed a bit since Lawrence of Arabia took it from the Turks by attacking the Wadi Itm defences, the key to Aqaba, by approaching them from the rear and across what must have been a nasty bit of desert in those days, well; it certainly looked that way in the film.

Jordan was a sleepy little country set up by the British, pretty much, in the 1920s. Thanks to Winston Churchill and T.E. Lawrence, the country started out as the Kingdom of Trans-Jordan, which is not particularly snappy and was changed along the way. Bordered by Saudi Arabia, Iraq, Syria, Palestine and Israel, or the occupied territories as to which they are often referred in the Middle East, Jordan has grown up a diplomat.

The young King Abdullah is shaping up to be as good an international diplomat as his father many would agree. Sadly, we would leave Jordan that day.

There was a ferry leaving Aqaba port for Nuweiba, Egypt in a few hours. They were Jordanian hours, which are longer than European hours, so we were in no particular rush. This is Jordan, three hours ahead of GMT and sixty-four years behind anywhere else in the country.

It was in the port that Chris and I met Dr Whiz.

Dr Whiz, not his real name, was a middle-aged man without the traditional moustache of the northern Arab. A medical doctor who had driven to Aqaba non-stop along the dodgy pipeline road that runs close to the border between Iraq and Saudi Arabia. That's a little less driving than Chris and I had done going via Jeddah - on his own - non-stop – without sleep.

We didn't have time to go into his story fully but suffice it to say he worked for a practice in the Emirates; he was an Egyptian going home to visit his family with a car loaded to the brim with all the stuff you could buy in the Emirates but could not in Egypt.

Chris and I had the sneaking suspicion after a few minutes in his company that the good doctor had been prescribing to himself.

His obviously dry mouth, hyperactivity and over-the-top talkativeness were a dead give-away to two guys who had been in his situation during their younger years. We might have been wrong but in the Port's offices his finger-tapping, lip-chewing, teeth-grinding, tongue-smacking and wildly staring eyes only confirmed it for us. It made him more interesting to us in any event. Weird meant we looked good by comparison.

Dr Whiz spoke Arabic and knew his way around otherwise we would probably still be in Aqaba. Off we went on another mini adventure.

It turned out, at that time, that you couldn't buy ferry tickets in the port. Don't laugh. We had to go into the city. Dr Whiz had the information and seemingly the chemically-induced enthusiasm. We hopped into a taxi and sped off at an unbelievable speed and even before Chris's door was closed. Unfortunately, for Chris, his door didn't close properly and through Dr Whiz the taxi driver explained that there was a piece of rope to do the needful. Normally this would be tied to the handles of both rear doors but now one of the handles was missing too. Just our luck to get a taxi driver who appears to be selling his car a piece at a time.

The taxi driver and Dr. Whiz were talking about us because I noticed the 'Ingleezi' word a few times. I also saw the driver look at us in his mirror. It was nice to know he used it for something, as it was under-employed in lane changing and corner turning.

Chris was sitting behind the driver holding on to his bit of rope, as he couldn't tell where to tie it in the absence of one of the handles when the driver swerved wildly into a right-handed turn.

"Jeezuss" I heard from Chris as he almost disappeared completely. I grabbed Chris's leg before he vanished out of the taxi. We were now a little scared as we got Chris back onto the seat and both held onto the bit of rope together. The driver and the good doctor were oblivious. Chris never said a word. He just looked straight ahead. He looked as if someone had just stuck a gun in his back.

We had to go to two places for ferry tickets: one for us and one for the car – but of course. The first ticketing place was a house and the office was someone's lounge with a desk placed somewhat conspicuously in the middle of the only rug in the centre of the room.

When we entered, Dr Whiz set about explaining what we needed. It is commonplace in the Middle East for anyone, who cares, to join in a conversation or a meeting regardless of whether it has anything to do with them or not. This incidence was no exception and we had the rest of the boss's family and neighbours checking us out within minutes and adding their opinions. We had to wait a while for someone to run off and get us drinks. Refusal is rude remember. We tried our Arabic out some more.

"Tatakallam Ingleezi? asked Chris" (Do you speak English).

"La," said someone. (No).

Chris has a dimple in his chin reminiscent of Kirk Douglas and this amused our host no end. "You are Cook," he proclaimed happily exhausting his English vocabulary on something so important.

We both laughed and nodded like lunatics rocking themselves for comfort.

We had tickets for the humans and after getting directions to the car-ticketing place, no country in its right mind would have both tickets sold in the same place - it couldn't live at that speed - our taxi driver, who came to get our tickets with us, sped off again.

We waited in the hallway at the next ticketing house as it was quicker and the ferry was due to sail in five minutes. Dr Whiz told us not to worry it was always late. On the way back to the ferry port, we bought ice at the Doc's suggestion, 'to keep our water cold.'

"We need to buy some water, Chris," I said.

"I guess we do."

Neither of us was old enough to remember buying ice even if they had had such a thing in Britain. This was something out of the Dark Ages. Huge chunks of ice were manhandled onto a slab and hacked up by hand. It was very cheap apparently. The good doctor treated us, as we still didn't have any Jordanian Dinar. We gave him some of our US dollars. I wouldn't want you to think we took advantage of our drugged-up buddy.

The ferry which was due to leave at midday eventually left somewhere around four in the afternoon. Loading the Nissan on was fun. Even the wing mirrors had to be folded back as space was that much of a premium. Hopefully we wouldn't need anything from the truck as it blocked everything in front of it and was totally blocked in by everything behind it.

We made our way up on deck, where we were allocated an oar and chained to a bench. Memories of epic movies depicting the Trojan Wars flooded my mind. The drummer at the back, there to keep time, while rowing was warming up by practising nifty fills and paradiddles; he looked a lot like Ringo Starr. It was basic, but we didn't really have to row and Ringo was as nice as pie to everyone. He didn't look out of place at all.

The ferry ride, supposedly a couple of hours, as the journey was only about twenty miles, hah-hah-hah, took forever. We only got deck tickets because we thought we weren't going to be on it for long. Dr Whiz had bought a first-class ticket, which we thought was a little strange at the time and an unnecessary expense. We visited him during the trip and he seemed a little down. This, we guessed, was because he was!

On deck, our travelling companions were labourers, lorry drivers, Ringo and so on. You might say we stood out a little, but in true Arabic fashion, we were accepted as part of the hive in no time.

We hadn't planned this part of the journey too well as we'd expected a Dover to Calais type affair. We were laughably wrong so many times. No fry-up, no cinema, no noisy little oiks running around causing chaos. What we had was much more fun.

No food and two bottles of water in our almost useless cool bag with the ice we had purchased with the good doctor was not a smart move for being outside for the rest of the day and not reaching Nuweiba port until gone 10:00 p.m. It was hot and we were shoulder to shoulder or rather our buttocks were cheek to cheek with our travelling companions. Forty-five-plus Centigrade in what very little shade there was, yes, you could say it was hot.

There was a little shop of sorts on the deck of the ferry but it only took Egyptian pounds and we didn't have any of those either. Not to labour a point but if we had been in any other country or region I might have worried.

We ended up sitting with a group of lorry drivers on their way back to Cairo. They had us enthralled with their stories. One of them had no tongue. It had been cut out as punishment for coveting someone's sister. The brothers did it and the guy had accepted this gross punishment because he would have done the same thing. Cairenes are nothing if not passionate I guess.

Blood feuds and honour killings are still happening in Egypt but mostly in rural upper regions. Two feuding families over the last decade or so have killed many on either side. They both live in the village of Beit Allam near Sohag. To illustrate the ferocity of these feuds, here's an example documented after our trip.

In 1995, twenty-four members of two families died outside a mosque in the Minya province. Three years later a man involved in the

1995 bloodbath killed seven and injured nine of his family's rivals. This is not a potato up the tailpipe kind of vendetta; this is family-tree-altering stuff.

Some of the past feuding somewhat predictably has been linked to militant Islamic groups. Having met and been befriended by many Egyptians I can tell you that they are passionate about just about everything in their lives, so whether it was religious, fraternal or otherwise probably has little bearing as these feuds go back a long way. Back to the ferry trip, which still has more in store for us.

The chap relating and translating all our travelling companions stories had a Bachelors degree in Economics from Cairo University but could only get a lorry-driving job in Saudi Arabia. His name was Mohammed; he seemed to be relishing his job as storyteller. We had to tell our own stories in return – quid pro quo. They wanted to hear about England, the green and pleasant pastures, the good life in the West. We made it up.

Once the ferry was off and running, our friends got settled and snoozed or played chess or cards. The card game was unrecognisable to us but we involved ourselves in the shouting anyway – churlish not to. Chris and I took turns in playing the whole group at chess, as Egyptians are not very good at watching any game quietly. We got out our ice-cold water and passed it around. No one wiped the top of the bottle as it was passed on but then neither did anyone's lips touch the bottle. Sharing is a way of life so all observe the niceties. When the bread and cheese came out a little later, we were part of the family.

Passion finds it difficult to be still, so if you coop up a horde of passionate males you have to expect a little drama. Ours came from an interesting source with an even more interesting outcome.

The little deck shop owner was overcharging his customers we found out after the scuffle broke out. It seemed that the proprietor was used to dissent as he was armed with a nasty looking little truncheon.

When Arabs argue there is usually a lot of shouting and normally everyone else joins in and takes sides. Someone acquiesces and the fracas dissolves. That is unless it gets physical. If you want to upset a Gulf Arab, you knock off his Ghoutra (head dress). He may then take off his sandal with which to hit or threaten you. Punches to the nose and head butts are so unseemly.

Weapons are unusual and the sight of a truncheon had everyone against the shop proprietor, well, he just wasn't playing cricket, was he. It looked as though he intended playing baseball.

He made a serious error in judgement in any event as everyone nearby rushed him at once. It's funny and scary at the same time to see a man suspended in mid-air by hands alone. Then we realised, they were going to throw him overboard. Chris surprised everyone, especially me. He rushed forward towards, the soon-to-be Red Sea swimmer shouting, "Hey! Hey! HEY! This is not going to happen." Mohammed was translating for those who didn't speak English, but hey is pretty much the same in any language.

Remarkably, the lynch mob, or should that be drench mob, was happy to listen to Chris because he had a good solution to the problem without anyone losing face – very important.

Chris negotiated a reduction in prices in exchange for this guy not to have to swim the rest of the way to Nuweiba. It really was quite remarkable. No one lost face except perhaps for the shopkeeper who was pleased to have dry clothing at that point.

A little scuffle occurred after that as the guy who had been initially threatened with the truncheon hit the shop proprietor with his sandal but that quickly died down. Chris fought his way back over to where I was still doing an impression of Munch's Scream; he had two glasses of mint tea the proprietor had given him free, presumably for saving him from the madding crowd. He would be far from them in no time.

"I'm shocked, Chris," I said and closed my mouth for the first time in about five minutes.

"Yeah," he said. "They were going to throw him in."

"I was more shocked at your getting involved . . . a little dangerous, don't you think?"

"Nah, seen stuff like that all the time on the pipeline – they're rarely serious," he said dismissively. "If it had been Brits or Dutch I'd have stayed well clear."

The rest of the trip passed quite pleasantly with our being beaten at chess very noisily. I'd like to say it was a tactical loss but I think we were no good playing twenty or thirty people at once.

It was the first real chance to lie back, in what little space I had with my hands behind my head to suddenly tense as the Dogsbane insinuated itself into the verse of losing my religion, that I was singing in my head.

Oh no, I've said too much

I haven't said enough

I thought that I saw your Dogsbane . . . That can't be right.

If I didn't give my father the stuff, I was wimping out. If I didn't give him the stuff, he might die in pain. If the tables were turned, what would I want him, or someone else, to do for me? I would want the option to choose when to end my life if I were terminally ill. Shit, coming to conclusions like that would not help my mental well-being. I had to give him the stuff.

What if the stuff, I even have a problem referring to its proper name, is taken off me at one of the Customs posts? My other wimpish plan. Then, I tried, it's not my fault. Perhaps the approaching land mass would be the answer to my dilemma. My step would be lighter perhaps and I wouldn't have to keep filling my head with inanities in a vain attempt to stop thinking about this stuff. Nevertheless, my list of strawberry-blonde-headed actresses with alabaster skin was getting longer and they were becoming more and more likely to bump into me while I'm on this trip. Because, they would be filming something on location and would be glad of the distraction - hey, it's my inanity and I can give it as much detail as I wish.

Once we reached Nuweiba we encountered a hold-up getting off the ferry because a car was in the way blocking most of the other cars. We should have known it was ours when we tried to fight our way down the stairs to the car deck. We were beginning to take such things in our stride and were definitely not surprised that it is difficult to get the car down the ferry's ramp, firstly because the ferry was not tied up properly and was moving about a lot, and secondly because all the new passengers were rushing up the ramp before anyone had got off.

It was an interesting ferry trip in an old rust bucket of a ferry. I would have recommended it but it sank a couple of years later with the loss of all cars, but not life I'm pleased to add. There are now much better and safer choices, including a fast Dover to Calais-style ferry, if you like that sort of thing.

By the time we made the Nuweiba Customs in Egypt we were convinced that we were being singled out for as many Customs-oriented difficulties as possible, even though no one had given a damn about my Dogsbane dilemma. Had it been taken off me, I wouldn't have had to think about giving it to my father.

The export plates and original paperwork were also at the root of our run in with Egyptian Customs and an unnamed official wearing a black leather jacket, who apparently worked for an Egyptian security force at odds with the local tourist police. Once again, due to the fact I couldn't keep two things in it at one time, the Dogsbane was forced out of my head.

Chapter Seven

"Papieren!" said the harassed man in his early nineties rushing along collecting everyone's travel papers.

Assuming fair-haired Western people are German is a common misappehension in the Arab world that has been open to tourism. Germans take many holidays, they travel a lot, they get many paid holidays, and so that is why often Germans get to all of the good holiday spots first. Many German towels were on many Egyptian sun beds almost every morning. Many millions of Deutsche Marks had helped the Egyptian economy, well, those that reached the Egyptian economy. It may be no surprise that Mubarak means 'happy/blessed/fortunate' in Arabic, eh Mr President?

As for being mistaken for a German, it's almost good not being tagged as Ingleezi right off the bat. "Ingleezi," I said, batting over our wad of papers.

"You have other papers?" The old man said, looking down his nose at the swathe of reconstituted Sherwood Forest I handed him.

"Nein!" said Chris, bristling at being called a German for some reason (perhaps the Second World War holds bad memories for him). "Wir haben sonstigen papiere." (We have no more papers). Chris's command of the German language was impressive. What a shame we weren't going anywhere near that country or any other one that speaks its language where such a skill might have been useful.

Chris's intended linguistic sarcasm was lost on the poor chap as he ignored him and looked at me when he said, "No more papers . . . OK . . . you wait here."

An inexperienced traveller to the Arab world would be feeling alright about what had just taken place. They would be thinking that the sweet old man had gone to sort out their paperwork. He would be back soon and they would be moving on. They would be wrong.

What had just happened can be a common experience in the Arab world. It can be peculiar to experience at first-hand the reticence to say no or disappoint someone. Such a mind-set has developed an intriguing filing system in the region. Real, or not, there are three trays to this filing system: in, out and the most important in this case: too difficult.

In the 'too difficult' tray go the things you don't want to deal with. The things that you hope, if you leave them, alone they'll go away. We had just been filed in that tray, which would slow our moving through Customs no end.

Being impatient in the Arab world is a deficit, as I believe I said earlier, my problem is that even though I know that, it doesn't help. In fact, I have Patience Deficit Disorder. I become so impatient that I do or say something stupid that delays me even longer. It's a vicious cycle but one that I ride with Armstrong-like skill and Quixote-esque determination.

When you see the fully laden shopping cart at the checkout with no owner, it's me – sorry. I'll shop for an hour sometimes, and then when a shop assistant holds me up for thirty seconds wanting to get something priced, because I picked up the only item with no price or barcode on it, I'll walk off in a huff. When I'm a mile down the road, I'll realise how stupid I've been. Being a jackass takes real effort and more time than most are prepared to give to it. What can I say? It's a calling.

Girding our loins for the inevitable onslaught, Chris and I decided to, temporarily; give our nonagenarian the benefit of the doubt. We leant against the Nissan and smoked quietly. Then we had another cigarette. The old ones are the old ones.

Chris looked at me as we finished our cigarettes and said, "This could get messy. After all we're dealing with a Muslim country that used to worship cats." He ground his cigarette butt into the ground with dogged enthusiasm.

"Should I worry about the things you worry about, do you think?" I said trying not to think about people on their knees praying to cats five times a day. "What the heck, if you're going to pray to something why shouldn't it be a cat, or a tin of baked beans, or anything else? Faith is faith, right?"

The Customs official hadn't come back; this was the run-around we were expecting. We gathered up everything we had 'papers-wise' and 'document-wise' and went to do battle with the Egyptians. If it was good enough for the Hittites . . .

As we entered the Customs building, we spotted the old man feverishly running this way and that. No one else seemed to be working. The office was dirty, walls and ceilings stained by cigarette smoke, when you could see the stains through the clouds of smoke, which were probably there 24 hours a day. No one looked up; no one came to help us. The so-called officials looked slovenly, surly, and adorned the office like industrial spillage. 'Welcome to Egypt' I uncharitably thought to myself.

Coughing to get someone's attention in here would be the ultimate in futility. Chunks of blackened lung could have been expectorated on to the blackening flooring. The old man eventually acknowledged us, probably because we seemed pitiful. He grabbed our papers and with us in tow disappeared into an office. Processing on almost all the other passengers was complete by now and things were slowing down – if that was possible.

The manager in the office examined our papers, quizzed the old man, peered at us, and said, "La!" (No)

He appeared the sort of person who wouldn't tell you the time in a watch factory. I could be wrong but usually only a few minutes either way. Dismissed with a wave of the hand the man went back to one of the three other conversations he was having simultaneously.

Over the next hour, we covered every possible angle of gaining entry to Egypt, with anyone who would listen to our story. We came up against poorly painted cinderblock walls reeking of nicotine wherever we went but we made ourselves such a pain in the rear that the Chief of Tourist Police in Nuweiba became involved. His office was bigger but just as filthy as all the others were. The low wattage lighting was reminiscent of many other municipal buildings in the region but his desk was large enough for a reasonable game of ping-pong. You know what they say about men with big desks, don't you? No, neither do I.

The chief was a portly man who couldn't reach his business card holder without coming around to our side of the desk, so that was probably why he didn't give us one. He was sporting the obligatory moustache and quite a bit of cheap-looking gold braid on his beige, wrinkled, food-spattered uniform that stretched tightly around his midriff. His belt buckle sat at a jaunty angle fighting against a belly of gargantuan proportions; he glanced at our papers.

The old man gave him chapter and verse. He quizzed the old man, as he seemed to be fighting our corner now by the tone of the conversation. We had spent so much time with him we must now be friends, that, or he simply wanted to get rid of us. The chief told the old man to tell us in broken English that the car couldn't come in to Egypt but that we could.

Oh, golly gosh, I thought, but using words other than 'golly' and 'gosh'. This is reminiscent of a conversation we had this morning in Jordan. We could not let Egypt get away with not letting us in; this was the main attraction as far as Chris and I were concerned and we would plague them until they let us in.

Tired, stressed and seeing our entire 'adventure of a lifetime' collapsing before our eyes I felt the beast of frustration within me stir. We were tired; it had been a long day and not a particularly great one at that. We had been hot for most of it and we were desperate for a cold beer and a shower. I'm not proud of it, but I lost my temper. Cover your eyes if you don't want to witness this unpleasantness.

"We are trying to spend thousands of dollars in your godforsaken country and all you can all do is say no; is this because you are not strong enough to say yes?" I said waving my wallet for extra arrogance. There was a rather unpleasant gob of spittle at the edge of my mouth to complete my most agreeable ensemble. He didn't have to understand what I had said as it seemed clear he understood the tone, I don't think he liked it but I wasn't in prison so . . . so far, so good. We were put back in the too difficult tray by being told to wait outside his office. At least this wasn't a 'no' and that is what one aims for in the Middle East. It was a long shot but right about now we were due for some good luck.

Losing your temper is a dangerous play in the Arab world but sometimes it is the only way to get any action. The action it usually brings is someone with more rank into play. We were on a slippery slope now if we couldn't get someone to sign off on our predicament. If we didn't push hard, we might not get in. If we pushed too hard, we could be facing other problems.

The old man was amazed at my outburst but didn't seem too unhappy about it; he was chuckling to himself. He said, "I will bring one man to see you."

We were left sitting on unpleasant orange waiting room chairs outside the chief's office. I hate orange chairs and anyone who would buy them I thought childishly. I smoked a cigarette to calm down. At least one part of my antisocial behaviour would fit in with everybody else.

"Are we prepared to forego Egypt?" I said to Chris.

"No, Jordan was a blow, but Egypt is the trip in a lot of ways. We have to keep at them until we find a way through. This is Egypt for God's sake everything is for sale."

"Are you suggesting what I think you're suggesting?"

"I don't know, am I?" said Chris, looking more serious than I expected.

"Shit, man! I really want to get in to this country but I would have no idea who to bribe or how much and my Arabic doesn't stretch that far, I don't think."

"Chill! Let's just improvise and see if an opportunity arises where we could offer to contribute to the widows and orphans charity or something," said Chris. He sounded worryingly crooked all of a sudden.

We settled into our own little funk outside the Headmaster's study, with thick books down the back of our trousers in case we were for six of the best. We were soon, however, to find out that the Headmaster had a nemesis.

After about 20 minutes, the old man returned. Walking behind him was one of the largest Egyptians I have ever seen, not carved from stone of some kind. His black leather jacket complemented the single eyebrow that seems to be getting more and more popular in this part of the world. He had an almost comically rowdy moustache underlining his Semitic nasal architecture.

The old man really was chuckling to himself now and the tune duelling banjos would have been a good backing track at that point. The big man had a voice to match his size and he asked for our papers. We told him they were inside with the chief. All we received was a "Tch." Chris and I both noticed that the big man's jacket didn't hide what was under it, close to his left armpit, too well. It's difficult not to stare.

"Ali (the old man's name, we'd been too wrapped up in ourselves to ask) has told me about you. There will be no problem. This man will change his mind," said our rather huge friend and now benefactor in absurdly cultured English.

"Are you with the Tourist Police," asked Chris – rather naively or mischievously.

I couldn't look at him in case he made me laugh and we blew what might be our last chance.

"No I am with . . . I am with the government," he said smiling. He shared the joke with Ali who thought it was hilarious and disappeared into the chief's office without knocking.

We heard some shouting and the murder of crows that had been congregating in the chief's office left quite quickly, mobbing the big guy seemingly wasn't an option. Scalded cats with firecrackers tied to their tails could not have exited with more aplomb.

This was getting interesting. The man mountain in leather was out in two minutes closing the door slowly but firmly behind him and making a head and eye rolling gesture in the chief's direction. Chris and I were not sure whether to laugh, cry or stitch a quilt.

I wanted to say something but all that came out was a rather pathetic, "Hee-ee-ee-mm . . ." Which is Arabic for my brain has obviously gone walkabout again, without me.

We both looked imploringly at the big man. He smiled at us and said, "He will change his mind, but you will need to give him something for security on the car." He added, "Give him some time to think, he has lost a little face."

He adjusted his jacket by its lapels, ran his fingers through his hair and theatrically smoothed down his moustache. Holding his chin for several seconds, he stared into middle distance and silently walked back from whence he came.

"Who was that moustachioed man?" one of us should have asked, but I was still mentally challenged and Chris, well, Chris was watching the big man being greeted by all and sundry as he walked through Nuweiba Customs.

We understood the need to give the chief a little time. The big man's English really was impeccable and he was obviously well educated – in all manner of things, I shouldn't wonder. It appeared he had swung it for us, but this was Egypt and hardly anything was as easy as it could have been.

Ali went off to get some tea and, after about fifteen minutes, brought one for the chief. As he delivered the tea, he ushered us in. The chief was not a happy man and was slumped in his chair more like overly mature Stilton than the rather large and entire Edam he had tried to come across as earlier in the evening.

"How much is your car worth?" asked the chief almost belligerently and glaring at Chris.

Chris deferred to me for confirmation. I was trying hard to think whether I should go high or low when it struck me that honesty is probably going to be best here. I love it when my brain works properly.

"About nine thousand dollars U S," I said. I had actually paid 33,000 dirhams for it so I wasn't far off with a UAE fixed conversion rate of 3.65. You really needed to know that didn't you, I can tell these things. Put that calculator away and just trust me.

"You will need to leave nine thousand dollars with me until you exit the country with your car," said the chief and he didn't even seem to be relishing the thought. I also thought his English had improved no end.

For Chris and me our elation at beating the chief was turning around on us again. In travellers cheques we had a few thousand dollars but we could get more the following day from the nearest ATM or American Express office. We looked at each other and were both probably weighing up our options for getting more money when it was my turn for a good idea. My brain was firing on all cylinders; I would no doubt pay for that later with a headache.

Some time before travelling to the Middle East, having been taken in by advertising, I applied for a gold American Express card. I earned enough but thought that I wouldn't get it as I had a poor credit history of old. At eighteen, I'd had a problem with credit cards, inasmuch as you have to pay them back and I didn't.

Nevertheless, my Gold Amex card took pride of place in my wallet because a gold card still meant something in the early nineties. You didn't get them free in your sugar-coated carcinogenic wheatie-bangs in those days. I saw the effect it had on people who wanted your money, prices went up, service levels went up and strangely, it did have some kudosback then. I brandished it now and hoped that Amex had been doing their marketing in Egypt. I shudder to think of what I said next.

"This is a Gold American Express Card," I said pompously as I brandished it about in front of the chief. "I can go outside and get ten thousand pounds sterling from any American Express related bank."

I think I heard Chris gulp at this whopping lie but I carried on regardless. It was actually an exaggeration rather than a lie. I could get quite a bit of money advanced to me because of my poorly researched credit check with Amex, but not here in Egypt and not in Nuweiba at nighttime.

"This is what I can do for you, Chief," I said warming to my role as confidence man. "I will write you a letter stating you can take nine thousand dollars from my Gold American Express card if I do not leave Egypt by a certain date. I will even leave you a photocopy of the card as testament to that and just in case there are any administrative costs we will leave a non-refundable deposit of five hundred Egyptian Pounds with you." The money I was offering was a bribe. So much for my being the shy retiring paragon of virtue I made out in the earlier paragraph.

It wasn't a long pause but it was long enough. This was the time in the negotiation not to blink and neither Chris nor I did, we didn't breathe either. Tumbleweed blew down the middle of the chief's office, the clock on the wall ticked inordinately loudly sensing the tension and a desert fox in the distance yelped as it was mobbed by irate crows.

The chief wanted to see my Gold card. He scrutinised it, turned it over in his hand as he turned over my idea in his mind. Another pause and the aching desire to swallow, cough or rearrange one's seat were all ignored.

The chief caved. He beckoned Ali and gave him a stream of instructions waving at us with the card and making writing gestures in the air. I almost burst into a chorus of 'Ding Dong! The Witch is Dead', but as I used to be asked, on a fairly regular basis, if I was gay, bursting into a Judy Garland-related song at this time would not help my macho credibility in any way.

He said, "You make letter, he will make copies of your card and your passports, and you will sign all of them."

"Yes sir," we both said almost too eagerly. Interestingly, he did now remind me of the leader of the Lollipop League.

We had a forced march of many miles to find the only photocopying machine in the whole place and made all the necessary copies. This is something to get used to in the Middle East – everyone wants copies of everything, but few people have a copying machine. Just buying a bag of jelly beans in the Middle East requires four passport photos, three copies of your passport, two attested copies of your marriage licence, whether you're married or not, and a note from both sets of grandparents stating, to the best of their knowledge, that you have never been caught drunk in charge of a manatee whilst riding a unicycle. I'm not making that up.

We found some clean paper, not as easy as it might sound, and I wrote a letter to American Express that I knew they would never pay any attention to, affirming that they should give the chief nine thousand dollars if the car didn't leave Egypt in thirty days.

We went back to the chief who had all his cronies back in the office again, he probably wanted to crow about his run in with the big guy. He was getting back his lustre and his feathers now seemed less ruffled. We gave him all the documentation he asked for and he had one last little surprise for us – of course.

We could have two 15-day passes but we must come back to Nuweiba Customs to renew the pass after the first 15 days. We agreed. We had no choice. We felt there was something hidden in this last little glitch but we decided that once we were in the country and moving around it would be harder to get us out. We got a scrap of paper with the chief's explanation in Arabic on it, and an official stamp, to bring back with us. The renewal we would deal with in15 days.

I was glad I'd forgotten to give the 500 Egyptian pounds deposit because I have a good idea where it would have gone, as that was my intention when I mentioned it. I don't know, the chief never asked, so perhaps my assumption was wrong.

With all the necessary papers together, Ali took us through the other bits and pieces of Customs in no time. He explained as best he could that the man in the black jacket was a big man (no kidding), a government man. This was funny to see little old Ali's rendition of a big man; it involved lots of stamping of feet and the holding of arms as if there were a large bag of shopping under each one. The big man didn't like the chief, why is still a mystery, which someone else is welcome to try to solve.

The truck was reloaded, the dogsbane was ignored again and we were ready to go. We offered Ali 50 Egyptian pounds (about GBP 10) for all his help. He refused it, but took ten after we insisted.

As we went to drive off Ali said in an incredulous tone, "Not five hundred pounds?" and laughed the laugh we'd heard when he brought the big man to our rescue. Chris and I laughed too because we knew who really ran Nuweiba Customs and it certainly wasn't the chief. It was late and we needed a hotel.

Tacky motels are the same the world over. This one had pastel colours on the outside as well as the inside. They couldn't give us any food, as it was too late; the kitchen was closed and locked. There goes another star from my rating I thought until they said they did have some cold beer – Egyptian Stella. Not to be confused with the real thing, which should not be confused with that Cola that makes the world sing or vomit or rot its innards? I still have a T-shirt that proudly states on the front 'Drink Stella – twenty million cockroaches can't be wrong'.

With a tin of baked beans heated on the gas cooker from the camping equipment for me and a pot noodle made with boiled drinking water for Chris and, of course, four bottles of cold beer, we ended our first day in Egypt.

We'd made it. Sleep overtook us like pantomime nightfall.

The odour of open beer bottles is probably not the best smell to start the day with, but at least we were in Egypt. Swinging my legs around from the bed to the floor, I planted my feet firmly into the puddle of soapy water emanating from the bathroom. The wildlife in the room that we hadn't noticed last night was unhappily swimming around. My face meshed in my hands I tried to process what was going on, as my brain's 1958 gearbox needed a little double de-clutching first thing in the morning.

Chris was in the shower and the curtain had had an argument with the shower tray, as they were keeping a healthy distance between the two of them. Measure twice cut once, my granddad used to say, but then he never put shower curtains up in any Egyptian motels - that I knew about.

In true Heath-Robinson style, or Al Heath-Al Robinson as he would be known in Egypt, the floor that was supposed to be gently sloped toward the drain centred in the bathroom was instead creating its own little aqua park by diverting the water into the bedroom. Nothing we could do about it if we wanted to be clean and this wouldn't be the first time this had happened judging by the high tide mark of the pleasantly pastel foam-backed carpet of the prefabricated motel-style room in which we found ourselves. All it really needed was rental by the hour, a coin-operated vibrating bed and a cheap mirror mounted on the ceiling to complete the dreadful picture I'm trying to conjure in your mind.

The elation of 'having one over' on the Egyptian Customs was still with us when we checked out of the hotel that morning. We paid over the odds and didn't really care; it would contribute to them rescuing the species stranded on a small island of carpet in room 104. The last thing

I saw as we left the room were some cockroach helicopters trying to rescue the smaller species from the humps in the carpet. More cockroaches with Channel 4 Cockroach News neatly stencilled on their carapaces surrounded them. I guessed there'd be film at eleven. They looked in control of the situation so I wasn't too worried about letting them get on with it. One should never interfere with professionals trying to do their job.

It was time to check out Egypt. And, hopefully, in the coming pages you will see what an incredibly ludicrous statement that was.

We were about to explore a country steeped in history, covered with temples, pyramids and populated with tens of millions of people – most of them in Cairo and most of them in cars, and most of them in front of us. We were also looking forward to sampling some of the best scuba diving in the world.

First, it was time for an adventure, as we hadn't had one for a while. We took out our map of Egypt, as the one for France wouldn't have been much good.

Looking at our map of the Sinai Peninsula, which was a big chunk of beigey-yellow paper that included a few contour lines. This was not a surprise and we noted two routes to the Cairo road, which was where we had decided we would go first. One route was the long way with a good road the other wasn't. We opted for the other. It cut straight across the desert of the Sinai, went past the burning bush, or the site of it, and then on to the Suez tunnel and across to Cairo on the African mainland.

Sinai did not disappoint our thirst for our particular flavour of adventure - people.

The Sinai is shaped a little like a heart. The road we weren't taking went all around the outside – safe and boring. The road we took went almost straight across. We found the turn off quite easily. It wasn't signposted to Cairo but we knew what we were doing, as in, we didn't really know what we were doing or care for that matter. It looked right in any event.

Five minutes along the road we met an Egyptian police officer who I thought could easily be Officer Khalid's brother. He wasn't of course, but the resemblance was remarkable. The officer flagged us down by waving his arm up and down as if stopping a bus. His hand was outstretched and the palm down, otherwise he would have been being rude. Palm up rude, palm down not rude. I have no idea why and religiously failed to find out why.

"Marhaba," (Hello, less formal) I offered as we drew close to him.

"Marhaba", he said quickly and added "Ben."

Either he was expecting someone else or I was missing the point. I thought I'd tell him that my name was Greg, not Ben.

I said what I hoped was correct, "La, ina ismi Greg . . . wa anta (No, my name is Greg . . . what's your name)?"

"You haff Ben?" he said again more insistently and then added, "Ben!" waving his hand around.

I pointed across myself to Chris in a theatrical manner, which is akin to speaking English loudly, "This is Chris," in true Brit style I over-enunciated as if I were talking to an idiot rather than a foreign police officer, "We haven't seen anyone called Ben."

Chris, a little more on the ball than I, said, "I think he wants a bitch." Chris was already dipping into the glove compartment, where we had some bens, but no gloves. He handed the pen across me to the police officer, who turned on his heel and went back toward his hut. Just before he went inside, he must have noticed we weren't moving and he waved us off and disappeared.

"You are kidding me, right?" said Chris astounded at the cheek of this guy. He put all our papers back in the centre storage compartment. All he wanted was the bitch formally known as 'Ben'.

"He probably needs to do the Telegraph crossword or something," I offered.

We moved on a few more miles taking it easy when we saw a neat line of rocks in the middle of the road, which was ominous. I gently swerved to miss them, which slowed me down even more thankfully, because they turned out to be a makeshift Egyptian warning sign to tell us the road had vanished a few feet ahead. Arab pragmatism again. Everyone knows the government's not going to do anything about the missing road overnight, in a month, this year, if ever so we'll put rocks in the road to warn people.

You could see where the road began again a few hundred yards further on but in between was nothing but sand and a few of the bigger bits of road that hadn't been washed away by the earlier rains. There usually isn't a lot of water in the desert but when it rains, it pours. Water skids across the desert like a worm-infested dog, taking out everything in its path and coating everything in the detritus it brings with it.

There was sand, lumps of tarmac and a track to where the road restarted. We joined it in our first off-road adventure of the trip. It didn't require us to engage four-wheel drive but we did anyway because we were excited and a little bit nervous. At that point neither of us was a master at driving in the sand and with no back-up car it would have been extremely foolhardy to try any driving too challenging. Being stuck in the desert, miles from anywhere, with only that little guy at the side of the road with a newspaper on his head for assistance, is a potentially lethal situation as quite a number of people find out each year.

"What do you do at the side of the road all day long with that newspaper on your head?"

"Middle Eastern Automobile Club, sir."

"Ah! It all makes sense now. Where are your tools?"

"It's your imagination; you didn't supply me with any."

The road went on like that for quite a way. You'd see a line of rocks and start looking for the way to the track, as sometimes it was obvious. This was a lot more fun than a highway. No music or air conditioning on and the windows down to get the full effect of everything we drove on making slow but fun progress.

As we approached what looked like an oasis a sign indicated a bend in the road going to the right. However, the more reliable sand track obviously went to the left, so we did. We drove through the oasis slowly with palm trees and acacia brushing the side and roof of the truck in places. This was not a time to worry about my paintwork even though the thought went through my mind. The oasis opened out and we decided to stop to take some pictures and check the map. No sooner had we stopped than two little shoe-less girls no more than five and six respectively were next to me asking for, "Baksheesh!"

Now, many guidebooks, and the less well-informed travellers, will tell you that this phrase is begging; that it means give me some money. It does in the loosest sense but it doesn't give you the truer meaning, which is far closer to 'share the wealth or share your good fortune'. This is far more romantic and makes the pestering by urchins much less painful for a while. If you are an Egyptian guide you hit the kids with the stick you have specifically for that purpose and they stop asking for anything. I remember similar situations from my childhood; my mother used a wooden spoon in fact to keep my sisters and me in line – d-d-d-didn't d-d-d-o m-m-m-me any h-h-h-harm. I didn't have a stick and the two little girls were so sweet with their long black hair, beautiful dark eyes and tanned skin. I gave them five Egyptian pounds each. They ask for more. I look around for a stick. They run away.

With the last few days catching up on us, Chris and I decided to get going to Cairo. Making it across the Sinai was fun but we were getting hungry and tired. We would pick up a snack soon and be in Cairo as soon as possible after that.

Chapter Eight

Picking up a roadside snack can be a hazardous pursuit for anyone travelling. Over the years, I've eaten some interesting things such as camel, horse and a Chicken Kiev that squirted hot garlic butter onto my girlfriend's blouse. The relationship was doomed to failure before that inasmuch as one can have a relationship with an improperly cooked Chicken Kiev. The relationship with that girlfriend was doomed to failure too because she started looking in furniture shops.

Eating a cheese sandwich that has a metallic taste is not recommended in any part of the world and let me tell you that Egypt is no exception. The roadside eatery was in a shack on the left just before you go into the tunnel to take you under the Suez Canal. Egon, if you're reading this, I recommend you give it a miss, mate. I'd rather eat KFC while I'm sober.

"That sandwich tasted quite bizarre," I announced to Chris. "I think the cheese was off."

"I'd never eat cheese in one of those places," Chris said.

"Thanks for the warning, but I think we're both going to suffer," I said as I rolled down the car window to the opening bars of Beethoven's fifth symphony from my rear end.

Pleasing methane melodies notwithstanding, crossing the Suez Canal through its tunnel, I had a bout of physical rumblings whose portent was that all was not well and that I would need some privacy and soon.

I don't really need to tell you that we were not about backpacking on this trip. Although we had a tent it was not our intention to 'rough it' until we got to Europe, when we expected it to start getting too expensive to stay in five-star hotels. But, even then, it would only be if necessary. We had both been making a good living in the Middle East with our tax-free salaries and it was our intention not to make the sleeping and washing part of our trip too hard on ourselves.

If you are wondering why I'm telling you this, it's because we were heading for the Sheraton Hotel and Towers on El Gezirah island in the middle of the Nile in Cairo – not exactly a travellers' hostel. Unfortunately, we didn't know where El Gezirah Island was or what the island was called and it would have helped if we had, because no one we spoke to called it El Gezirah.

El Gezirah Towers Hotel and Casino is a round building and a bit dated in some ways even in 1991 but still quite luxurious. The way my bowels were complaining a wattle and daub hut would have been sufficient. I didn't know how long I had, before the world would drop out of my bottom.

Both of us had been to Cairo before but always by plane and then driven to where we were going by taxi. Actually doing the driving into and around the city was different. To give you a clue P.J. O'Rourke in his super book, Holidays in Hell, which didn't have any pictures in it, described the car horn as the Egyptian break pedal.

Signposts were rudimentary and if you didn't know the districts of Cairo or read Arabic you were pretty much left to fend for yourself. We'd been spoiled in the UAE with dual language signposts.

After getting ourselves into a few backstreet situations, none of which included boy bands I might add, we decided to stop being stereotypical 'men' and trying to find our way to the hotel by penis-power and ask for directions. The shapeless disorder of Cairo's streets was just too much for us.

Asking for directions is relatively easy in many countries, whether you speak the language or not, but in Egypt they hate to admit: one, that they don't understand your Gulf Arabic (or loud English) and two; that they have no idea where the place is.

Ask a policeman my grandma always used to say especially when she had no idea what you were asking her about, a response that increased as the years rolled by. So we did, and they were wonderful, friendly, and wanted to engage us in conversation, and they had no idea what we were talking about.

We were asking for the Sheraton Hotel on the island in the Nile – it meant nothing in English and we may as well have been ordering pork scratchings in Arabic.

Cairo has no rules for driving. As the saying goes, Allah (God) is the only traffic cop. There are social niceties to adhere to such as use your horn at every possible opportunity. With one foot on the dash, one on the gas and occasionally the brakes (if they work), one hand should be nonchalantly draped out of the window with a cigarette in it and the other checking out your hair in the rear-view mirror. This leaves it up to your prehensile genitalia to do the steering, which explains why most drivers in Egypt are men and why there are so many accidents. See an empty spot of road and make it your own – fast. A careful driver is one who honks his horn when he goes through a red light. My only quandary with all my extremities in use was how to keep the horn honking all the time. My one tip for drivers in Cairo, apart from don't, would be forget the new car and have steel bars welded to the outside of a halftrack.

Chris tells me that the bumper sticker on his local churchwarden's car reads - Drive carefully! Remember, it is not only a car that can be recalled by its maker.

In the dictionary next to the word shambles is a picture of Cairo. It was fascinating with disparate road and building styles jumbled together one could choose a road and start walking in the 1990s and end up back a hundred years or more in a brisk pre-prandial promenade. Sharing the roads with donkeys, cars, donkey and carts and pretty much anything else with wheels, legs or that could be dragged was nerve-wracking and more by our ridiculous good luck than judgement we ended up at our goal. After our accomodation for the previous couple of nights, we felt we were ready for some luxury – sad really, but then we never pretended to be William Dalrymple or Wilfred Thesiger.

Our tempers from the driving were in need of a little emotional blanket-stitching, which would probably come in liquid form, but if I didn't get a bathroom soon nothing else was going to matter in my world.

Pulling up outside one of Cairo's main five-star hotels was a dusty and dirty four-wheel drive with two spare wheels chained and padlocked to the roof and piloted by two unshaven dusty and dirty fellows who looked as if they had been chained to the roof. Dirty old dock shoes; sun-faded shorts, polo shirts and hand-tied rather sporty paisley ghoutra set off the whole ensemble. Just what an owner would want to see pulling up at his fancy-schmansy hotel.

Chris stayed with the car because they were trying to move it on from the front of the hotel. I went inside to get a twin-bedded room with a nice view. You couldn't blame them for wanting to move us on but Chris's countenance was meaner than a junkyard dog after the driving around Cairo. No valet was seriously going to take 'that' on.

Reception staff of hotels the world over always look you over as you approach, when they're not playing Tetris under the counter, that is. With surgically implanted smile, they appear as if they are gauging what sort of room you'll want or afford, or is that my paranoia rising again? This chap squinted at me with barely concealed horror that I would even approach his reception desk trailing a small cloud of dusty sand and giving the impression of being a reject from a Star Wars movie.

"I'd like a twin-bedded room for two people with a nice view please," I blurted out even before I had quite reached the desk.

He was already tapping away at something under the counter and shaking his head. He was going to tell us that they were full – I was ready for him though with enough bits of plastic to build my own Michael Jackson.

"Something with a view," I reiterated with what was probably a slightly unstable edge to my voice. My Amex and gold Sheraton card were already on the counter. It did the trick but if I'd have had more patience I probably would have got the same room for a lot less, but patience was thin on the ground after the day's driving.

Our friend behind the counter ushered us off to a private check-in on a higher floor, gave us juice and sat us down while our room was prepared. We were relieved of many dollars for the privilege, we were so pampered we almost stayed a second night but considered saving the money and paying off Rwanda's foreign debt.

We were on the twenty-fifth floor. Three more floors up and we'd have been on the roof. I was beyond caring I had found a bathroom. Marble, gilt, scented hand-towels, flowers, mouthwash, and barely audible chamber music - quite a toilet. Perfect for the noisy and malodorous pebble dashing I was just about to undertake. I sat there for some time and took more Imodium. Unlike George Michael, I do not like spending too much time in toilets accessible to other members of public.

The balcony and view were pleasant and very high so I didn't really go outside due to a rather nasty case of vertigo. I'm actually not frightened of the height; I'm frightened because I want to jump when I look over the edge to the point where I pick a spot to land. I know I'm not the only one with that condition because an old friend of mine in Dubai used to have it too, but he still lived on the nineteenth floor. He died of cancer at thirty-nine so he probably should have been worrying about something else.

Chris and I slept, washed and made the room look like a pigsty quite quickly. We ordered room service and caught up on the things we had promised to do, such as journals in my case. The Dogsbane took pride of place on the dresser.

In the evening, we went in search of fun and beer. We found the beer in the hotel but for the fun we had to wander around a while. Indeed our fifteen-minute taxi ride that we negotiated hard for brought us to the club at the back of our hotel. We didn't realise that immediately. Once we'd been turned away from the club for not being a couple, no sniggering please, we decided to take a stroll, and as we rounded the corner we realised where we were.

Our taxi driver had been so nice he'd complimented us on our Arabic and bargained hard for his fare. He had taken us on a tour of our hotel district and brought us safely back to within spitting distance of Reception. It wouldn't be the last time. After a few beers, we were now back in the hotel again we turned in and got ready to look at the Cairo museum in the morning.

Before going to sleep, I called my sister Jackie, the anchor to my family, to tell her I was fine, Chris was fine, the car was fine and that that everything else was fine too, oh yes, and not to tell her about the Dogsbane, that was no longer on the dresser.

"Dad is being a pain in the rear end about his treatment and not doing what he is told," she said.

"Nothing new there then," I said.

My father's second wife, Ann, a woman not easy to like, with leg hair so long it could be plaited into a resemblance of Mount Rushmore, was supporting him unreservedly. As she was only one year older than Jackie, and one year younger than my other sister Lyn, she was young enough to probably rather not want to face such a mammoth task as caring for a dying husband thirty years her senior but there she was.

Right or wrong, I didn't want to deal with any of that right then. I was still in the mindset that I wanted the Dogsbane to be found by Customs, which would appease any guilty feelings I might have toward my father. Then I could get back to not thinking about him very often. I hadn't realised the Dogsbane was not where I had left it, yet.

Chris and I were actually coming back to Cairo in a week or so to meet friends and celebrate Chris's thirtieth birthday so we would take a quick look at the museum probably and then take a leisurely drive to Luxor. Our friend at Reception had booked ahead for us and got us a Nile view room at a reasonable rate, Rwanda would have to wait a while longer.

In the morning Chris said, "I can see the Pyramids, if I lean right out over the balcony."

"Are you trying to make me feel sick," I mumbled into the shirt that wasn't fully over my head. I left it there shrouding my eyes because I didn't want to see the view. That's not true, I wanted to see the view I just didn't want to see how high up I was.

I held on to the window frame and could see smoggy, dusty Cairo off in the distance. It was enough for me. We left the hotel and went to see the museum. We reckoned that Luxor would take four to six hours to drive and we should get there before dark. We would set off at about 2 p.m. when everyone else was taking his or her siesta. Clever huh? We thought so.

You already know that the best-laid plans of mice and men 'aft gang-agley' and that our plans are not our best-laid ones. We did set out for Luxor on the dot of 2 p.m. and, before we set off, we saw the museum you have to see if you go to Cairo. But, the drive was more than we expected.

The Egyptian Museum of Cairo is an assault on the senses in that it has such a wealth of artefacts. There was so much to see it was crammed in and to me is almost reminiscent of a junk shop except this litter was thousands of years old. When you walk in the main entrance and look ahead to the atrium, you immediately know that this is going to take longer than you thought. Even with the Coptic or Christian 'monuments' as they are called having been moved out of the museum the span and scope of the undertaking is immense.

"Egypt has approximately one third of the entire world's monuments," according to Chris. Where does he find this information, and why?

It would not be particularly interesting for me to give you a run down on the museum and its contents. There are so many other books for that. I enjoyed the museum very much but, as is my way, I can't help searching for the quirky or out of place. I needed to look no further than the official guidebook.

In the official guide, 1988 version still in production I believe, it says the clerk at the ticket office is not obliged to give change. This does not mean he or she categorically will not give change. It's simply that this is another Arabic phenomenon. No one has change, really.

The Egyptians were one of the Nationalities to set up the bureaucratic system in the Middle East and sadly, they learned it from the British. This system has been refined to a Zen level of frustration over the years by Egyptians and Subcontinental Asians races – all trained by the British, so it's a little bit difficult to complain. The British and their empire have a lot to answer for even if they did build good railways. I continued to look through my guidebook.

At the museum, the Guardians, which makes them sound like a stone statue that will burst into life, like something out of a Sinbad movie, rather than somewhat tatty security personnel, have orders not to converse with visitors; a bit like a guard at Buckingham Palace but without the big furry hat.

The guidebook was not a lot of use, as it didn't tell you where anything was; it had a brief explanation next to a number that corresponded to the piece you may be looking at. My guess was no one knew where any of this gear was anyway. I started studying stuff from the rather minor Pharaoh Tutankhamen, and not being impressed checked it up in my trusty guidebook. Item 1050 was a stick with grips decorated with bark, oh really. Item 1051 was also a stick, but this time decorated with gold foil. The next item didn't have a number and when I looked closely, I could see that this is because, although it is a stick, it is used for holding one of the museum's windows open.

Quite a few mummies are housed in the museum and although it's difficult, I will not make any attempts at jokes about that. If you look at them, you would not want to make jokes either. These people do not look well. Items 6342 to 6366 are all mummies and you can get up close and almost personal with all of them. King Merenptah was the only one with a vestige of a grin. He was probably only smirking because he was not ground up for use by European doctors to cure some ridiculous malady during the Middle Ages.

Being a surgeon in ancient Egypt could be a little dangerous as a profession. If you lost the wrong patient, you might well have had your hands cut off. Chris was ready with some information too.

"People used to shave off their eyebrows as a way of mourning for pet cats that had died," Chris said as he walked past me.

Perhaps Chris would have been better off as a guardian, I thought, but said, "What's with the cat fetish?"

He signalled expansively with his arm. Cats were important in Egypt, that much could be seen at the museum, which displays many busts and sculptures, some of them more than a bit eerie.

I have since visited the museum on a number of occasions and although it hasn't changed much over the years my perception has and I have to say that the more one learns of Egypt's museum in Cairo the more your mind is blown. Every piece you see 'lying about' is a valuable artefact. This is the issue. Sitting in one area and learning about the pieces in sight, from a talkative guardian who may or may not be several Egyptian pounds better off now, is overwhelming.

Every piece you look at is so historically important it is almost impossible to fathom. Everywhere you go in Egypt it is the same. I remember seeing a garden wall made from blocks covered in hieroglyphs that could have been 10,000 years old. This would be analogous to wrapping your fish and chips in the Mona Lisa. With so much tangible history lying all over the place, it is taken for granted.

Chris and I wandered and 'oohed' and 'ahed' in all the right places, we hope. Before long, it was time to hit the road.

We went back to the hotel to check out and as we packed up the last of our things I suddenly realised I didn't have the Dogsbane.

"Chris, did you pack my jar?" I said still not verbalising what it contained.

"No, that's not something I really want to get involved with," he said.

"Oh shit! I said. "It's gone missing."

Now before you think I had anything to do with this I'll tell you I didn't. This was not the way I wanted it to go missing, were it to go missing. This did not suit my plans at all.

We searched the room. We turned it upside down - nothing. I called housekeeping and told them my problem, as in, my jar of very special cream had gone missing from my dresser.

"What make was your cream sir?" the housekeeping person on the other end of the telephone said.

"It wasn't a make; it was a special blend in an unmarked jar brought all the way from Abu Dhabi," I said. "And, I want it back immediately please."

Housekeeping offered to make enquiries of its staff but that they had gone off shift now. Blowing my top was not going to help but I asked to see the duty manager.

After explaining the story to him and explaining how the cream also had medical properties that were important to me, the manager assured me the cream would be found and returned the next day.

"I will be in Luxor tomorrow," I said.

"Ah," said the manager. "Can we forward it to you?"

"No," I said. I really wanted to force the issue but couldn't bring myself to do so. I asked him to please find it and keep it until I returned to Cairo in a couple of weeks. "This is very important to me," I said. "I will be very grateful to whoever returns the jar to me." The underlying thrust of what I was saying was not lost on the manager.

"It will be here waiting for you on your return, Inshallah," said the manager.

"Inshallah is not good enough I'm afraid," I said. "I want you to call me tomorrow in Luxor and leave a message that you have my cream. I am going to write a letter to the general manager of the hotel detailing what has happened and I will copy you in. I want that cream back."

The letter was a good idea because now the manager's promise would be in writing. He would have to deliver or face his boss's wrath.

I was not happy but also not bouncing off the walls. I felt remarkably calm and believed that what was meant to happen would happen. I was not going to let the Dogsbane rule my life. Chris and I leapt aboard the truck; he gunned the engine, the front wheels lifted high into the air and we left the hotel in a cloud of smoke and neighing tyres. They may have heard us shouting, Hi ho, Silver! Away! But I doubt they were even listening.

One of the pleasant things about driving down the Nile road was that we were not treated to the tedium, visual or otherwise, that was commonplace in the Saudi leg of our drive. Life was going on all around us. I noticed a smell in the air too, distinct, not unpleasant but difficult to place at first. It was the smell of forgotten times a smell that would have been smelt in most countries at various times throughout its development – wood smoke. It was not isolated, the smell was everywhere outside of the city. Cooking and any other heat came from burning wood. That's a lot of wood when you consider the population.

The number of people living in the country is at about 72 million in

2003. Arable land accounts for only 2.85 per cent of the 1 million square kilometres or thereabouts, a permanent crop 0.47 per cent, the rest, about 97 per cent, is desert and very much like Saudi Arabia. With a population a tenth of that size, the country might be self-sustaining, but under this amazing pressure one wonders how the country even survives.

Five or six thousand years ago, the concentration of land to live on was around the Nile, the longest river in the world according to my Collins atlas, and protection by the deserts was a good thing. It allowed the country to flourish and become strong.

Then almost two thousand years ago, the Persians took over followed by the Greeks, Romans and Byzantines. In the seventh century, once Islam had been invented just across the Red Sea the Arabs took over for the next six centuries, well, things had been a bit of a mess, why not give the Arabs a turn.

A local military caste, the Mamluks took control in about 1250 and continued to govern after the conquest of Egypt by the Ottoman Turks in 1517.

The Suez Canal really put modern Egypt on the map in 1869 and made it interesting to the major world power at the time, and the country has been in debt pretty much ever since. I wonder if that is a coincidence? – Nah!

The British in 1882, ostensibly to protect its investments (surprise, surprise) and because that's what Britain did in 1882, seized control of Egypt's government, but nominal allegiance to the Ottoman Empire continued until 1914. Kicked into touch in this region by the British and the Arabs the Otto-men got out of geo-politics and went into end of the bed furniture. They were very big in armless and backless padded seats.

Partially independent from the British in 1922, Egypt acquired full sovereignty following World War II when Britain gave up nearly all of the countries under its control, because it was made to by the new superpower on the block.

Unfortunately, or not, depending on your view, little of the order associated with the British Empire, especially where roads and their uses are concerned, stayed with Egypt. I believe I may have mentioned this already but driving in this country is terrifying and Chris and I intended to do quite a bit of that.

"This driving is harrowing," said Chris. "Let's try and only travel during daylight, eh?"

"Yeah," was the best reply I could muster as he was avoiding a fully loaded ten-seater van hurtling toward us on our side of the road. I was busy pumping my right foot and trying to climb backwards into the rear of the truck.

"These idiots just don't care, this is like playing chicken," Chris's voice was up a few octaves

Our four-to six-hour drive became an eight-and-half hour drive and we didn't get to Luxor until after dark. Even after sharing the driving we were frazzled.

Now driving in the dark in Egypt, even on what must be one of the major roads through the country, was an experience. We didn't expect it to be an experience akin to Russian roulette, however. We were used to red traffic lights having no meaning now and roundabouts being more like speed bumps. We were even used to donkey and cart teams and their suicide U-turns. What we weren't ready for was that the main road down the Nile to all parts south was nothing much at all. Two lanes of shoddy tarmac for the most part. Once out of Cairo proper we were in the countryside.

Driving down this road one could see the poverty so prevalent in Egypt. Many people were living hand-to-mouth existences even taking drinking water from the Nile in some places opening the possibilities of dysentery, cholera, Hepatitis A, typhoid fever, intestinal worms and polio.

Egypt, with such a large population is poor with a GDP per capita, although slightly improved is still hovering around, what can only be described as, a vulnerable $3,000.00.

The natural hazards of Egypt are not pleasant either with periodic droughts; frequent earthquakes, flash floods, landslides; heat, a driving windstorm called the 'khamsin' that occurs in spring; dust storms and sandstorms. An earthquake measuring five on the Richter scale occurred in June 2003, the epicentre was just northeast of Sohag so that will give them something other than blood feuds to think about.

Egypt isn't the only country in the world to have blood feuds but it does have a history of them. In fact the Egyptians have been around so long they have a history of just about everything. The one time in their history when they were wealthy and powerful was still all they had going for them now, apart from some petroleum and cotton exports.

Indeed, things haven't gone too well for the country since that big Exodus about two thousand or so years ago and I believe it was written that Egypt would never have it so good again. Difficult to believe all that religious mumbo jumbo but things definitely have not been on the up in Egypt for some time.

Egypt has long been an important interface between Middle East and West, leaders such Hosni Mubarak have played that quite well over the years. It has not always been a popular thread to follow for everyone in the country. The occasional tourist would be killed or abducted but nothing on the scale of the 1997 attack in Luxor, where Chris and I were headed, when fifty-eight foreign tourists and four Egyptians were murdered by Gama'at al-Islamiyya or the Islamic Group.

The movement's political agenda has a predictable ring to it, which is to topple the government of President Hosni Mubarak and establish an Islamic theocracy. The Luxor attack brought Islamic extremism in the country to the fore again, which hurt one of the biggest revenue generators for Egypt, tourism. Having tourists lying around in pools of blood with bullet holes on television is not a great advertisement. They'd rather we lay around in other pools.

Incidentally, the spiritual leader of the Islamic Group is none other than Sheikh Omar Abdul Rahman, the fellow who had the first go at destroying the New York World Trade Centre towers. Perhaps if he had driven more often between Cairo and Luxor he wouldn't have been trying to blow things up so much as he would have been a gibbering wreck, as we were, from driving after dark.

So that Chris and I could have the full scary experience in night driving the other drivers on the road got together to teach us new game, one that we had never played before or are likely to again.

Chapter Nine

Driving along the Cairo to Luxor road where the view above was remarkably like a Parisian avenue with trees arching overhead and dark greenery everywhere, Chris and I noticed it was getting extremely dark, no-streetlight dark. The comparison with Paris stopped when you weren't looking upwards.

The drive to Luxor had already been entertaining and spotting the little vans that carry nine or ten people horrendously mangled at the side of the road had became a macabre version of I-spy. Overtaking seems to have taken over from chariot racing. Fortunately, we had no nasty wheel bosses to contend with, but that was because on a two-lane road there isn't enough room for them with three cars travelling in alternate directions side by side.

I learned driving at night in England. If you need main beam, you 'dipped' them when a car came toward you, out of courtesy. If you forgot, it was the full glare of the oncoming driver's headlamps for you. If you are the oncoming vehicle, just hope that you have the brighter lights if you play that game. I tried it with a Rolls Royce once and was seeing spots before my eyes for days afterwards.

Chris and I learned a new style of night driving. First, lights on cars are not switched on until it's almost fatally necessary i.e. it's pitch black. This conserves two teaspoons of petrol per year for the entire country; the considerable loss of life is inconsequential.

Like good little Europeans, we put our lights on as soon as dusk appeared over the horizon. The first car coming in the opposite direction flashed his headlights at us.

"What's his problem?" said Chris.

"Perhaps there's something wrong with the truck, like a spare is loose or something, let's check." We were so naive.

We stopped to check the car was OK, it was, and decided he was from Bahrain via Saudi, and was squirting vodka on his windscreen he must have been unfamiliar with the controls on the steering column of his car. It could happen.

Not many cars were around so when the next car came and flashed his lights at us we offered encouragement to sexual and directional movement because this wasn't funny any more.

Now it was dark and there were no streetlights except in the (ha ha) built-up areas, represented by seven houses, a telegraph pole and a mangy dog that tried to chase us.

We saw a car approaching in the distance with its headlamps on normal. We felt comforted. A few hundred metres in front of us the car switched its headlamps off – completely – it disappeared.

"Where the freaking hell did he go?" shouted Chris.

"I-can't-see-him," I sang like a nervous purple dinosaur.

He was hurtling toward us for all we knew. Chris stamped on the brakes, screeched to a halt at the side of the road as the car came level with us, put its lights back on, and continued on its way. After a couple of these vehicular Russian roulette games we were . . . tense, but trying to get the hang of it.

We tried to work out if there was some sort of system to this madness as it happened with all the cars approaching. We tried flashing our headlamps, we tried switching our lights off, I couldn't see a thing Chris squeaked and hastily rearranged his furniture. I wasn't too confident about driving blind alone on a stretch of road just outside Luxor in pitch black. This slowed us down but we got to Luxor in one piece.

Our nerves were somewhat shot as we pulled up at the Luxor Sheraton and 'Stella' was the cry once we'd checked in. Alcohol would be the only way we could deal with that journey, half-crazed and addled as we were. Alcohol and an activity more anodyne than driving was all we wanted, we headed for the bar.

At check-in, I asked if they had any messages for me from the Cairo Sheraton, they didn't.

We met a man in the bar when we were having a nightcap, an Egyptian who was more English than Chris and I were put together; we must attract them. I'm still rather embarrassed that so many other people can speak my language yet I cannot speak theirs. He was researching a book on Middle Eastern history and we got talking about Palestine and the problems of the region. This is a staple conversation for Arabs particularly with non-Arabs with open ears and minds.

This chap knew his history and at least initially sounded completely balanced. It was interesting enough for me to take notes while he was talking. We were both enthralled by his compelling if somewhat biased musings. He was incredibly plausible and didn't lose his temper with two slightly inebriated Brits asking stupid questions.

"The Arab's view on the Jewish claim to land formerly known as Palestine is based on a biblical promise," said Hameed. "In the Bible under Genesis chapter 17 verse 8 we read:

"'And I will give unto thee and to thy seed after thee, the land wherein thou art a stranger, all the land of Canaan, for an everlasting possession; and I will be their God.'"

I am also impressed with people who can quote difficult passages from literature and other books, such as the Bible. "So this is all about a two-thousand-year-old promise made in a version of the Bible?"

"Yes." Hameed went on to explain that one could also read this claim in the Jewish holy book, the Torah. His eyes were starting to make him look a little mentally unstable when he quoted verbatim:

"Because Jehovah (God) was pleased with Abraham He wished to give the seed (children) of Abraham the land of Canaan as an everlasting possession." The quote is left hanging in the air as Hameed goes to relieve whatever pressure it is he's under. Chris and I believe that he is giving us, what sounds like, the low down on the start of all the trouble in northern Arabia. It's not that simple of course.

The Jews then argue that they are the people to whom God gave Palestine as an everlasting possession because they claim to be the Children of Abraham through Isaac. Hopefully you are still with me on this because this is where it gets interesting. And, no, I didn't know all this; I had to look it up afterwards. Some of my notes seemed to represent the energetic throws of an epileptic spider as it crawled from an inkpot.

Hameed, treating the ice in his glass to a lesson in centrifugal force explained that, "The Jews have conveniently ignored Ishmael, the first son of Abraham and his children. He is supposedly denied Palestine because he was the son of a slave woman, called Hagar, whereas Isaac was the son of a free woman, Sarah."

Now the only Hagar I have ever heard of is a Viking in the comic section of a British newspaper.

"The Arabs are the children of Ishmael of course," added Hameed in a conspiratorial tone. "But that is not the best of it."

So, if you follow Hameed's line of reasoning, which with a somewhat booze-addled brain was not that easy, the Arabs have the greater claim to the land in the north unless slave women don't count, which I thought was quite possible for that time as slaves were little more than possessions. He had a line of reasoning for this too.

Hameed, who was savouring his single malt whiskey, and knew that Chris and I were sitting waiting for 'the best of it', said, "In the Torah it states that the firstborn should get a double portion of his father's share, even when his mother has a lower status."

And, the Bible backs this statement up in various places such as in Deuteronomy. He couldn't remember the exact verse in Deuteronomy but I could forgive him for that as I thought Deuteronomy was a character from the musical 'Cats'. I certainly wasn't listening in that lesson of Religious Education. I believe children learn about more than one religion these days in British schools, which is nice. I'm sure Hameed would approve.

You had to listen to this chap because he was so knowledgeable. His logic was compelling. I had no idea the argument went back so far and had so much depth and texture. It would appear when listening to Hameed that the Jews were ignoring their own holy book and neither Chris nor I had the knowledge to counter his excellently put together argument if we had wanted. I have no doubt in my mind that there is a counter argument somewhere, of course. With the way the Israelis behave, with American support, these days, the argument may be, "Because we say so!"

You just have to feel a little silly when Hameed asks why the so-called civilised world has recognised a two thousand year-old Jewish argument that contradicts the faith's own main religious text. Chris and I both find the bowl of peanuts and trail mix, or whatever it was, very interesting at this point. Hameed is watching us squirm and I believe this is not the first time he's done this little number. We order more beer.

He continues: "The present day Israelis are almost exclusively European Jews who have migrated, settled and ousted the original population. Many murders take place with American armaments while the Palestinians throw rocks. Does it seem fair to you?"

"When you put it like that," offered Chris, "no, it doesn't." Very diplomatic, I wish I'd have thought of it. However it wasn't perhaps what Hameed was looking for!

Hameed's face and posture changed and even tensed as he leant forward to blow his calm exterior. "The European Jews were disgusting animals and hated by everyone. Hitler killed thousands of them, which is not good, but the Holocaust wasn't anywhere near as bad as the Jews made out."

Chris and I are exchanging 'why us' glances at this point. Hameed was on a roll and thought he might as well stick it to the Brits while he was at it. Apparently, the British offered Palestinian land to the Zionist movement for fighting the Nazis. He went off on a particularly nasty anti-Zionist tirade after that, which we couldn't bring ourselves to listen to, we made our excuses and left as soon as humanly possible.

As we made our escape Chris asked, "What did you think of that?"

I replied a little slowly that, "I wasn't too keen on the last bit but he did make a lot of sense, but after numerous Stellas I think Prince Phillip, whom I love for his outstanding ability for putting his foot in his mouth on the most public of occasions, could make sense about now." I added, "I'm going to read up some more on this when I'm back in England though; It'll be nice to have access to a library and real bookshops again." I also thought that if I end up in prison for murdering my father, at his request, I'd have a lot of time for reading, when I wasn't being someone's girlfriend or whatever it is that goes on in prisons these days.

At least we were in Luxor, the place that so many tourists are dying to get to.

Luxor, western Thebes the whole area is fantastic in a touristy kind of way. It has almost as much to repulse you here, as it does to attract you, which seems to be a constant theme in the Middle East. There is relentless harassment for money, to buy cheap knock offs of scarabs and such like, tacky shops and if you are female watch out for tactile males. They like bottoms here, but it is not the bottom-pinching capital of the world. We had yet to reach that part of the world.

A strange thing happened to me at one of the temples, which although felt a little spooky at the time its full spookiness didn't register until I was back in England. So, bear with me, I'm laying the groundwork for a spooky experience later on in the book.

It went like this. Beggars, would-be guides and plain urchins with their hands out always pester you when you go to the temples. So I was not surprised when a man entered my physical space telling me that he was my guide. I brushed him off, he kept on, I brushed him off and he kept at me. He had the foulest breath and the scariest teeth - not out of place in a Stephen King novel I shouldn't wonder. Chris could see I was getting flustered and starting to lose what little cool I had.

"Hey! Come on, buddy, we don't need you," said Chris.

"You need a ticket to come in," said Tombstone Teeth. It turned out he was the official for this temple and we had to buy tickets from him. He made extra money by harassing tourists into hiring him as a guide. He was obnoxious.

We gave him the few pounds it was to enter the site but he still wouldn't leave us alone.

"Can we have the tickets please? I said, "And then you can go away." He was getting under my skin and no matter how we tried to ignore him or lose him he just kept coming at us. It was freaky.

We ended up going around the temple, where we were still the only visitors unfortunately, in double-quick time.

Just before we left I said, "I'd like our tickets please." We were keeping all our memorabilia.

We still hadn't given this guy any money other than for the tickets. He held the tickets up in front of my face and tore them in half. In a split second, my head filled with that familiar rushing buzzing sound and the drummer, also in my head when he's not in Viking longboat movies, sounded attack speed, quickly followed by ramming speed. I went for him.

Luckily, for me Chris saw it coming and got between us because I'm sure I would have caught something from him bleeding on me. He held me back as all the veins in my body tried to attack this oaf on their own. Tombstone Teeth laughed and leaned towards me giving me the full force of his unclean and unkempt countenance and said, "Are you angry English?"

My reaction was as if he had struck me. I have no idea why those words jarred as much as they did but I could feel shivers going up and down my spine. I tried to calm down as Tombstone Teeth walked away without looking back.

Chris said, "Come on we've lots to see and there is no point being locked up in an Egyptian jail for murdering someone who will probably die from halitosis at any minute."

We walked on but I glanced back at the temple from time to time until we were out of sight.

This is without doubt one of the most important archaeological areas on the planet, as if you need me to tell you that. If you want details on every tomb and so on you are going to be disappointed but one of the most interesting questions about Egypt I wanted to find more out about was how on earth did they build all this stuff. I didn't find out too much but what I did find was interesting.

Chris being the most civil of civil engineers that I knew was happy to help me in this area.

He explained: "Contrary to popular belief, the treatment of workers at the valleys was good considering we are talking about a few thousand years ago. They were fed well and had days off and worked a reasonable number of hours in a day. Ten days working and two days off - more for religious festivals, which doesn't sound so bad. Some people in the 'developed world' are not treated that well even today."

I was thinking of Razwi, the 'tea boy' from Chapter One. In truth, I can see the workers of today having something to say about the conditions but I prefer this more humane mental image to the one Hollywood and others portray of everyone being beaten, crushed and generally abused. Not a good way to motivate, I should imagine, especially if you are trying to get your tomb built within a timeframe even if that timeframe is a lifetime. Short lifetimes were a habit in Egypt thousands of years ago. Take Cleopatra, a clever kitten, but she was bitten on the asp and died quite young.

Succession was a big issue in the old days. Nomination for next in line was a bit like the kiss of death. Still, plenty survived the description 'evening and morning star' such as Rameses in the cartoon 'The Prince of Egypt'. As you can see, I have spared no pain or anguish in my research.

"Would you say that Pharaohs were obsessed with death?" asks Chris. "You've just been made Pharaoh and the most important thing on your agenda is your tomb."

"Nothing wrong in looking ahead I suppose," I added. "It was probably good for the economy, gave everyone a sense of purpose and stopped them from starting wars."

The building of a tomb, after the first few, went like clockwork it would seem. The surprisingly good detail of recording this whole process fell to some top-notch civil engineers. With the location decided, drawing the designs, as well as decorations, the main architect would get on with the job. Design meetings with the client were a little boring.

"Stepped or smooth your God-ship?"

"What did Sheepslegshut have?"

"He had stepped, but the smooth is immensely popular these days Your Infiniteness, the really important deities are having gold tops put on."

"Ohhh! That sounds nice, I bet it's expensive."

"I can do a special price for you Your Divine-ness and it won't cost you an arm and a leg, as long as we don't have to be buried in the tomb at the same time as you, your hugeness."

The artisans often divided into two groups, right and left, to add a little competition to the proceedings. There would be specialists such as stonecutters, plasterers and sculptors. The process was pretty much like an assembly line from that point. Quarrymen, led by John Lennon, dug the tomb before they went on to become The Beatles, the plasterers smoothed the walls, and draughtsmen made the designs on the walls approved by the priests and the Pharaoh would sign it all off. The losers bought dinner, or were fed to the crocodiles, when they weren't practising running in a zigzag, which was the latest fashion. The artisans, that is, not the crocodiles.

Using red ochre to divide the ceiling and walls up into a framework, or grid, the pictures and text emerge in the right places. A chief draughtsman would check it all and correct it with charcoal, which is how tic-tac-toe was invented. Sculptors cut the bas-relief and painters would finish it all off. It is more involved than that but the abridged version is still smooth. Many of the tools of the day such as sticks with decorated handles, plumb, bob-the-nebti-shovels and tri-squares are in the Egyptian museum, if you know where to look.

I liked the way the old and the new mix with one another in Luxor even more than they do in Cairo. In Cairo, it was a catastrophe but in Luxor, it exuded charm. A walk down the corniche or Nile-front from the hotel one walks past felucca stations, the boats traditionally used on the Nile, with the captains all offering tours and special prices to take you anywhere you want, within reason.

We passed modern hotels and took in the sights. As we walked along taking it all in a voice came from behind that said, "G'day, mate."

Both Chris and I turned, expecting an Aussie traveller looking for directions, a light for a cigarette or something else. What we saw was five foot six of fellah (Egyptian for peasant/farmer) with a huge grin. Enter Abdul Rahman a well-known character in Luxor. He owns a few donkeys and knows the hills and valleys around the west bank of the Nile.

"Salaam alay koom," we offered.

In the broadest Aussie accent, Abdul Rahman said, "Narce Arabic, guys, whed'ja learn that?"

Whatever he was selling, we'd already bought it.

It is still so strange to me to meet someone dressed in dish-dash with an 'other world' accent. It reminds me of an Omani friend of mine who has the broadest Texan accent. The first time I met him, in a business meeting, I was ready with my faltering Arabic. He leapt out of his chair and strode toward me, dressed in full National regalia, including a khanjar (dagger) tucked in his belt, with outstretched hand saying, "Hi, howya doin'?"

Chris told Abdul Rahman we'd lived in the Gulf for a few years and we carried on a conversation as we walked. We booked him for two days heavy-duty, donkey-backed sight-seeing. He would meet us from the ferry in the morning. He was gone as quickly as he arrived.

"Well that's that then," I said. "it looks like our sightseeing is sorted out for us."

"Yup," said Chris. "Donkeys? Very Biblical."

"What, don't you have any interesting facts about donkeys?" I said taking a small but niggling dig.

"Up yours."

Abdul Rahman had learned his Aussie accent from a bloke who had spent a lot of time in the region doing research who had used him a lot for his wanderings. He was a superb salesman and boy were we pleased we were signed up that way. In the morning going to the West Bank, of the Nile not Palestine, it was a huge bun fight. Guides, beggars and so on accosted us every few feet. They would pester us on the ferry, which is, according to Abdul Rahman, illegal.

Wandering across the Nile you can look back at the splendour of Luxor, Western Thebes. In its history, it had been the centre of the Egyptian world, a synonym of extravagant wealth and, even with the amazing sites on display; ancient pictures that still survive offer a furtive glimpse of the majesty of the world's greatest open-air museum, telling us that much is still to be found.

Chris examined his notes and said, "This used to be called 'What'sit', before it was called Luxor or Thebes."

"Why would anyone call a place What's-it? That sounds like they couldn't make up their mind and really doesn't sound ancient Egyptian to me." I was beginning to think that Chris was losing his marbles somewhat.

"Not, What's it, W-A-S-E-T, What's-it," he explained peevishly.

"Oh! Wass-it, not What's it," I indicated my understanding.

There seemed to be a little tension building between Chris and me. A day in the saddle should sort it out. I suppose it was only natural that we would tire of each other's company from time to time. Prior to this trip we didn't really know each other that well. We'd been thrown together and so far had made the best of it. Some beer and a heart-to-heart to lay some belated ground rules would probably be a good idea, but we didn't do that until much later on. We kept busy and stayed in our hedonistic groove until we were ready to lift up our emotional skirts, so to speak. Being shallow and emotionally aloof has its advantages I find.

When we got to the other side, it was bad, but there was Abdul Rahman with a helper who shooed all the flies away. He walked in front of us and hit anyone in range with a stick. It wasn't a decorative stick. It was merely a stick. The stick seemed to work well at keeping people away from us, however. There is only a very slim chance but, maybe one day, in the distant future; this could be in a museum and its guide.

Item 1020 - a stick, used for hitting people - It was not understood why sticks were used in this way but it is generally accepted that it was a form of greeting the indigenous population by wealthy travellers from far, far away.

Once we were past the melée, we got down to talking about where and more importantly how much. Silly us, we hadn't negotiated a price before we had agreed to go with him. You can fail bargaining 101 at Parsimonious High with mistakes like that. It is so important to bargain in the Middle East. There is no honour in accepting the first price offered or in beating someone down to where they won't make a reasonable profit. Although tell my wife that. I'd never seen a shopkeeper cry before we were married.

Abdul Rahman invited us to his house for tea before we set off. The house was a shell, no windows, bare concrete floors and no plaster on the walls. His wife and daughter served us tea and offered us food then retreated to the west wing, well, the kitchen actually. It wasn't proper for them to be in the room at the same time as us. The Arabic way of life is a misogynist's dream world.

We accepted the tea and took a rain check on the food as we had just eaten breakfast; also, if honest, we were scared of what they might serve us and could tell they didn't have a lot to give away. A baby slept on the small rug on the floor in the room where we took tea, but eating that would have seemed greedy and unseemly. Nevertheless, a couple of lazy flies helped themselves to anything they could find on or around the child. Abdul Rahman was poor, proud of his family and passionate about his job. We were confident he would be a good guide. He was.

We had a tremendous couple of days with Abdul Rahman. We took tremendous shots of all the things one needs to and got sore rear-ends from the donkey riding. We went into tombs and paid bribes to photograph inside as everyone else does. The smell of urine in the tombs was common and spoiled many of the places we visited. No matter. Egypt is one of the places in the world you must go to, forget Europe and the Far East, Egypt is the place to go. And if you see Abdul Rahman say hi from us. His donkeys were real characters and they didn't mind that we were the real asses.

Chris's donkey it turned out wanted to be the leader but nearly always started at the back when we stopped for rest or photography. It overtook in all the scariest places. Chris had a tough time hanging on to the donkey while careening around a wild bend seemingly hundreds of feet up above the Ramesseum at one point. Such an endearing mental picture is difficult to erase. It was reminiscent of a Warner Brothers cartoon. His near misses with death were highly entertaining.

When you look at pictures of the Valley of Kings, you will notice a high and steep cliff skirting the valley. We rode around it on our valiant steeds peering down on the kings before descending to their tombs. Dismounting to take pictures over the edge of the cliff, I hardly ever wanted to jump because the scene was so compelling.

We gave a huge tip in Egyptian Pound terms to help Abdul Rahman buy some windows before the winter came. We had tea with him again before we left and I don't care if he swindled us or not. The value we got from meeting his family and understanding more about Egypt and the people was easily worth what we gave him. His simple life seemed to fulfil him and his children adored him, you could tell from the way they greeted one another. A slight envy pricked me from somewhere deep within.

"Live long and prosper," I said to Abdul Rahman, giving him Spock's Vulcan salute as we parted. He handed us over to his stick bearer to get us back to our own side of the Nile.

Chris shook his hand and thanked him profusely.

Abdul Rahman smiled and said, "Good-on-ya, mates! You've got a few kangaroos loose in the top paddock, but enjoy your walkabout. She'll be Apples."

Which in Arabic I think is, 'Ha ha ha! Crazy, crazy Ingleezi.'

With the sun going down and the shadows lengthening, it is easy to see why Luxor is and has been such a draw for people from all walks of life. Even in the midst of a summer, crowds appear, but Egypt has changed a lot over the years, never more so than with the plague of humans both indigenous and otherwise. The great travel writer Baedeker in his 1929 guidebook talked of verdant crops rather than overcrowding and the murder of tourists as a high point in Luxor. Although he would be condemned with the majority of his views now as being condescending and politically incorrect, his observations on modern Egypt would make interesting reading.

I called the manager at the Cairo Sheraton to be told he had gone on vacation. That, it would seem, was that, for the Dogsbane. This was really going to help my father and I resolve our differences before he died. And, damn me if I didn't feel guilty about that now. We checked out of our hotel the following morning to head for Aswan to see a big, a really big dam.

Chapter Ten

In the two days we had spent in Luxor, we forgot what the driving was like in Egypt. Visiting temples and qahwa vendors along the way sorted out jangling nerves however. The Turkish coffee they sold was like drinking a highly flavourful hot and gritty mud. It was also tantamount to applying jump-start cables to sensitive parts of one's anatomy. It would be difficult to be more awake.

The warm welcome received from these shopkeepers and the rustic charm of their establishments far outweighed the dowdy and dusty disposition of their outlets. Every customer is a friend and not only by the servers but by the other customers too. Chris and I were an unusual sight, which is vaguely pleasurable in a country full of unusual sights.

Everyone wanted to know where we were going and then why. We were 'crazy Ingleezi', we were getting used to the title, and I have to say it made me feel like a young schoolgirl catching a boy taking a second look, my chest puffed up a little more every time. Crazy Ingleezi to my mind meant slightly eccentric but somewhat courageous – maybe that's dreaming but they really did think we were crazy.

The everyday Egyptians are lovely people if you'll permit another of those sweeping statements but, the country really is in a mess economically with poverty rife and it seems to have been that way for quite some time now – about two thousand years. You can read about this problem in the Bible.

Ezekiel, you'll probably remember he wrote that great speech for Samuel Jackson in the film 'Pulp Fiction' (Ezekiel 25:17),well, Ezekiel had it in for Egypt it seems and prophesied that the King of Babylon, who was named after a champagne bottle twenty times its normal size, would give Egypt a jolly good thrashing.

To quote Zeek, as he was known down at the local ranting club, "I will put an end to the hordes of Egypt, by the hand of King Nebuchadnezzar of Babylon."

As ever he got carried away a little after that, "I will make the land of Egypt a desolation among desolated countries; and her cities shall be a desolation forty years among cities that are laid waste. I will scatter the Egyptians among the Nations, and disperse them among the countries," he ranted.

I believe he got 'rant of the month' for that one. Claiming the words were directly from God he looked a bit sheepish when it didn't happen quite like he said it would and to rub salt in his wounds the King of Egypt at that time, Aahmes, ruled for another generation over a prosperous Egypt and lived to see Nebuchadnezzar die. (Only a few Egyptians were scattered or dispersed in the making of this story, mostly ones that no one really liked very much).

Ezekiel would probably have been quite comfortable in our modern times, he even sounds like he may have been a bit like Al Sharpton or Ian Paisley who use a thin patina of religion to cover other intentions. Of course, Zeek may have been the tub-thumping, soapbox standing-type of preacher but perhaps he would even be a hot-tubbing, cocaine sniffing, womanising TV evangelist, difficult to call. His prophecy sounds to me like he was perhaps licking one too many agitated tree frogs.

Incorrect as the prophecy may be, and we're skipping details of course, but it did all pretty much go down hill for Egypt not long after that little episode. There have not been too many things to shout about for a long time. Perhaps there was a grain of truth in the prophecy. The country went into some form of a holding pattern, for nearly two thousand years. The next time they tried anything big was in the 1950s when Nasser seized the government by military coup and tried to build the United Arab Republic, even with Russian backing that was all in vain.

Resting on one's laurels for two thousand years is however a neat trick. Moreover, the temples and monuments built during Egypt's heyday will remain outstanding for as long as they are up standing. On the way to Aswan, we stopped to see one of the best examples of Egypt's 'outstanding-ism'.

Edfu is truly amazing. Chris read from his notes that he had been working on with some other guidebooks recently. "A Ptolemaic temple, the best-preserved major temple in Egypt, it is dedicated to the falcon god Horus and took 180 years to build."

For the hard of hearing and those at the back I'll repeat that; it took one-hundred-and-eighty years to build. Just a little longer than it took my father to build a garden shed that fell down the day the wind changed direction.

Chris continued, "Construction began in 237 BC and completed around 57 BC."

To break that down that's about six generations in Ancient Egyptian terms as the average life expectancy was 30 years, you can check that with Chris. In fact, the construction spanned the reign of six Ptolemys. They stopped for a breather of twenty years due to unrest during the period of Ptolemy IV and Ptolemy V. Dynasties . . . hah . . . can't live with them, can't live with them.

Buried under sand, a lot of sand, which did a great job of preserving the Edfu temple, it was uncovered in the 1860s by the chap who helped to uncover the Sphinx, namely the somewhat cavalier French archaeologist, Auguste Mariette.

One of the more surprising and frustrating things about Egypt is that there is still so much to discover. It has important archaeological finds under almost every patch of sand and the Red Sea still has many tales to tell.

Pictures and words would do no justice to the magnificence of Edfu. This is not only the best preserved ancient temple in Egypt, but the second largest after Karnak, the one that pops up in all the movies such as James Bond's 'The Spy Who Loved Me'.

"You can see the main pylons of Edfu, at one-hundred-and-eighteen feet high, from the Nile," offers Chris. "The temple was built on the site of the great battle between Horus and Seth. Hence, the current temple was the last in a long series of temples built on this location. The original structure housing a statue of Horus was a grass hut built in prehistoric times."

"You like all this stuff, don't you, Chris?" I said. "All the facts and history and so on."

He stopped reading and stared into middle distance for a moment, "Yeah, I do; is it annoying?"

"Not at all," I lied. "I couldn't be bothered with it. It's interesting and I'll tell you to shut up if I've had enough, OK?"

"Sounds fair."

This is about as close as most men get to a heart to heart. Had we been in the locker room there might even have been a little bottom slapping, although, as someone regularly approached by homosexuals for some inexplicable reason, I get nervous at any male-to-male physical contact. I'm comfortable with my own sexuality but my Gay-dar does not seem to work too well. I'd be wary as hell in the Roman baths.

There is a small Roman settlement nearby to Edfu. It would probably be something one would visit in any other country. But, it looks like a jumble of hovels compared to Edfu, then pretty much anything would, some German tourists were using the Roman buildings as an al fresco toilet.

Why would Romans build a bivouac by such a mighty temple you are probably clamouring to ask me? Well, they had to have somewhere to live while they tried to hack all the faces off the reliefs, not in a fit of pique, but because they were an affront to their own religious beliefs. Ah religion! The answer to all things.

Chris and I are there in the blistering July heat but are humbled and chilled by the numerous and amazing reliefs, some of which are intact, including a depiction of the 'Feast of the Beautiful Meeting'. This is the annual 're-union' between Horus and his wife Hathor. During the third month of summer, the priests at the Dendera complex would place the statue of Hathor on her barque, a ceremonial barge, and would bring the statue to Horus's barque at the Edfu Temple, where Horus and Hathor shared a highly spiritual conjugal visit. Each night, the god and goddess would retire to the Mamissi, or the berthing house. Edfu is a must-see when in Egypt. Well, you're not going to see it in Benidorm now, are you?

From Edfu we climbed aboard our trusty Nissan Pathfinder and headed for a big pile of concrete holding up a lake in Aswan. One of the only high points of Egypt's recent history is the Aswan dam. Chris was firing on all cylinders that day. "The completion of the Aswan High Dam in 1971 and the resultant Lake Nasser have altered the time-honoured place of the Nile River in the agriculture and ecology of Egypt."

I have to be honest in this instance. The Aswan Dam is incredibly boring to look at unless you are a civil engineer interested in things to do with water. Now . . . where would I find one of those?

For Chris it was love at first sight and he reeled off more statistics than I care to write down here. He did seem quite fixated in facts. Suffice to say the dam was a high point for him. Wandering around, re-hydrating and smoking, I thought I'd get Chris away from his facts for a bit.

"I can't help thinking it was a smart thing for Egypt to do rather than pursue nuclear energy as Iraq did in the late seventies and early eighties," I said. That stopped him in his tracks; he smelt some facts on their way.

"How so?" he asked, his interest piqued.

"I am glad you ask zat," I said in my best French accent, which is a cross between Adolf Hitler, and Dick Van Dyke. "Zee French, promised oodles of money for zee nuclear reactor, built it eighteen miles souse of Baghdad. Zee reactor was called Osirak, after Zee Great Oz who landed zare in his balloon after overshooting zee Emerald City on a trip from Kansas."

"So what was the problem with that? I don't see what you're getting at," said Chris, starting to study his notes again.

With the French accent ditched because it was awful and too difficult for me to do while I was thinking, I said, "The much-needed seventy-megawatt uranium powered reactor was near completion but not stocked with nuclear fuel when Israel bombed it to smithereens in 1981, because they saw it as a threat to their country." I added with a bow and a flourish, "They probably would have done the same thing to Egypt."

Chris was interested. "So the Israelis believed it was for making nuclear weapons?"

"I guess so, but it is a little difficult to believe, as the French are permanent members of the UN Security Council, surely they would not have allowed something like that to be built by one of their own companies in a country so allegedly threatening to world stability, would they?"

"Good point," Chris conceded. "Wasn't that around the time Israel confessed to having the capability of developing its own nuclear weapons?"

"You are on the money," I said. "In eighty-six, I believe, Mordechai Vanunu, a former Israeli nuclear technician, was found guilty of espionage after he told the Sunday Times that Israel was secretly building atomic bombs."

Vanunu, imprisoned for espionage for a decade or two is in and out of Israeli prisons still. While Israel is, in spite of everything, the only nuclear enabled country in the Middle East, which we know of, and the only country in the world not independently monitored by the global atomic watchdogs, the International Atomic Energy Agency (IAEA). You remember them, the ones who entered Iraq to look for Ws of mass destruction or else the United States and a coalition of the less than willing would invade.

Here's an interesting titbit. One of the pilots who carried out the attack on Osirak was, Ilan Ramon, who trained as Israel's first astronaut would die in the Columbia shuttle disaster in 2003, which could be a popular one for the conspiracy theory junkies.

Chris had returned to touching and looking the Aswan Dam. I am not even there.

I have a pet theory that there is no way of checking, but here goes. I believe that even if someone solves the issue of Israel and Palestine the region would still be in almost as much turmoil. Arabs have never been good at playing nicely together. Even in the go ahead United Arab Emirates, for example, they can't even decide on a federal road traffic policy, in as much as, what vehicles can drive where.

There is an line in a film I may have mentioned once or twice. Lawrence is on his way to meet up with Lord Faisal and he stops at a well with his guide. Enter Omar Shariff, as Sheriff Ali, and soon we have a dead guide. They were from a different tribe that's all; like being from different families or different parts of the same country. Like someone from Portsmouth killing someone, because they come from Lincoln.

Lawrence: "Sheriff Ali, so long as the Arabs fight tribe against tribe, so long will they be a little people . . . a silly people, greedy, barbarous and cruel as you are."

There are many millions of Arabs and they have a great deal of money, ask the Bush family of Crawford, Texas if you doubt me. If they were organised they'd be a major force but, as they can't even decide in one country between two relatively small emirates how many lanes of traffic their trucks should use, uniting against anyone or anything regionally or globally seems unlikely. I wonder if that will ever change.

Chris being the energy expert between us explains that energy is an important problem in the Middle East, due to rapidly growing populations. More countries are going to want to go nuclear as it makes the most sense. However, if a nuclear power station is going to be bombed out from under you it doesn't sound such a good deal I suppose. Building dams like Aswan would be a great idea if the Middle East had any water of which to speak.

Having seen a few dams in my time, and even having built a few across the stream at the bottom of the road where I grew up, Aswan is boring and has nothing to look at other than a huge slab of concrete.

This is not going to stop Chris who tells me that, "The Aswan Dam stopped the Nile flooding, it generates power and keeps the crocodiles under control on the Lake Nasser side of the dam, mostly."

Mentioning Nile crocodiles aloud and in front of other bored tourists wondering what to look at, brings a mini audience for Chris. He stopped stroking the concrete. He said, to anyone listening, "If you get chased by a crocodile, run in zigzags because crocodiles have a problem turning sharp corners; it was all the rage in the old days."

The other tourists move on, I wish we could, but Chris hasn't even got started yet.

"Egypt claims Aswan is the driest city in the world with its annual rainfall averaging 0.02 inches," says Chris with his notebook open.

"Well, it doesn't have a lot to offer unless you have a concrete fetish," I reply and decide not to listen to any more facts about Aswan. Trying to let Chris indulge himself and make love to a dam was not a highpoint for the day, but it takes all sorts, right!

There was little for me in Aswan, sex with inanimate objects is dead boring. But, in Aswan until we found the Cataract Hotel, which was wonderful and straight out of an Agatha Christie novel. In fact, Murder on the Nile came to be at the Cataract. The Hollywood birthing pains managed to change quite a bit of Egypt for the film unfortunatel. You know, move some monuments and temples about. Well, they thought it would help the story and what would ancient Egyptians know about the placement of monuments for a modern film anyway.

The Elephantine Island in the middle of the Nile is quite beautiful; we could see it from our hotel room and decided to check it out if we had time. Still I had been a little disappointed with Aswan but I was disappointed in style now.

If you are going to take the trouble to go to Aswan, and I guess you should, make it memorable and splash out. You will not be sorry. Having travelled a lot and having been fortunate enough to have stayed in some great hotels in the world I would put this one, built by someone called Thomas Cook, in my top three. Book early and be careful, as more than one Cataract Hotel exists. Primarily don't let anyone palm you off with the New Cataract Hotel; this is a concrete travesty too close to the old one for comfort. The new one is a 1950s concrete office block next to St Paul's Cathedral, a foam finger vendor under the Eiffel Tower. Once you've seen the original Cataract Hotel you'll wonder how the other monstrosity got planning permission but then I am applying logic, which often has no bearing on property development in any part of the world.

The hotel is gorgeous so Chris immediately started making notes and reading all the leaflets. According to records, the Old Cataract's first newspaper advertisement appeared in The Egyptian Gazette on 11 December 1899 and promised all the modern amenities of the age including 'electrical lights running all night'.

The Cataract has a long and distinguished list of guests in its history including Czar Nicolas II, Margaret Thatcher and Howard Carter who celebrated his find of Tutankhamen's tomb there. Carter arrived late one night to find the hotel door locked. It didn't have a night bell; it had a horn outside the door with a little sign that quite spookily said, 'Toot and come in'.

Sir Winston Churchill was a guest at the inauguration of the earlier and smaller Aswan Dam, Agatha Christie too as mentioned got the inspiration for a book but allegedly she was troubled by a new class of ne'er do well in evidence – the tourist. Other greats to grace this outstanding hotel include the Aga Khan III, King Farouk of Egypt, the Shah of Iran, Jimmy Carter, Queen Nour of Jordan, Princess Caroline of Monaco, and Princess Diana who apparently had a penchant for Egypt and things Egyptian right up to the day she died.

While the hotel has several restaurants, the '1902' is one of Egypt's most famous eateries. Chris and I decided to try it.

In our best, crumpled, yet unstained trousers and shirts, with sleeves and buttons, we made our way to dinner. A warm welcome waited, and the staff seemed keen on us drinking a lot. Being the shy retiring types that we were, we let them get the better of us and we may have drunk a little too much. Before I tell you why we shan't go back there I'll tell you about this restaurant, because it is something else.

Designed as a Moorish hall, the domed restaurant features four red and white traditional door-key style arches with stained glass and exquisite mashrabiya. This is a distinctive type of wood carving particular to the Middle East mainly used for windows, which allowed cool breezes to enter homes in the heat of summer and as you are no doubt aware by now is very important. Another way of cooling a home in the region was a wind tower. Constructed 5-6m (16-20 feet) above the house and open on all four sides they act as primitive air-conditioning units. Often wet sacking hung inside the tower to help with the cooling. They didn't have wind towers at the prestigious 1902 club they had good air conditioning.

The back of the menu that I was already having difficulty in reading told us that the 1902 opened to celebrate the first Aswan Dam, a British construction, and the Khedive Abbas Helmy, the sovereign of Egypt under the Turks, attended the opening night. Winston Churchill attended with King Edward VII's younger brother, as well as dukes, lords, possibly Lord Lovell, and other dignitaries so we may have been in good company. We didn't see anyone we recognised.

The food was good but I wasn't so sure about the entertainment that comprised a male Nubian dance troupe followed by an incongruous group of female dancers who got a conga going. I was beginning to understand Agatha Christie's fear. Chris and I were totally bemused. We were perplexed when we realised that we were up and dancing in the Conga too. We shan't go back there, as once is enough. Dear Agatha must be mortified.

Turning in for the night and soaking in some of the ambience, that didn't involve me kicking my legs sideways while holding the person in front of me by the waist; it was easier to appreciate the lure of Aswan as a destination. The climate must be one of the main reasons for Aswan being on the map in modern times, enough of a breeze perhaps to make it bearable in summer, whilst in winter a jacket would be necessary. The gentle scent of flowers from time to time and one of the most stunning rivers in the world drifting by less than a stone's throw away made it . . . dramatic pause for a puff of a cigarette in an unfeasibly long cigarette holder and in true Noel Coward style . . . tolerable.

Morning, it arrives in a most similar yet opposite way to night. A dimmer switch turns on at its lowest level ignored for a while, then someone decides its morning and it is in a big, bright and hot kind of way. The view from the room at The Cataract was quite something to write home about, so I did.

Breakfast on the balcony is not too shabby, it was possible that I could get used to such hardship. And, at that precise moment my father and his Dogbane insinuated themselves into my mind.

Writing postcards to family seemed like a lie. Having a wonderful time. Weather is here and wish you were lovely, etc. Smuggling some stuff back for Dad so that he can kill himself, but I lost it in Cairo. Look forward to seeing you back in England. With love, Greg.

It really was doing my head in having to think about this stuff and even if I got more how could he be so blithe about it?

"Chris, can I talk to you about something?" I said reluctantly.

"Is this about your dad and the former jar in the car?" he said matter-of-factly.

"Uh, yeah," I said after removing the Dr Seuss image in my head - car in the jar indeed.

"It messes with my head every time I think about it," said Chris. He'd obviously thought about it a lot.

"Would you do it for your father?" I asked, looking for someone else to shoulder some of the weight I was carrying.

"No, but I'd stick a shotgun to his head and pull the trigger!" he said with more malice than I thought possible from him.

"You and your father not best buddies then?" I said trying to bring the conversation back on track.

"He used to hit my sister, my mum and me. I wouldn't piss on him if he were on fire. But that doesn't help you, does it."

"I don't get on with my father but I do think I might piss on him were he alight. I would probably make a point of telling him that I had done it however," I was still trying to lighten the conversation a little.

"Look, Greg, the way I see it is this - your Dad's asked you a favour, a big one. You feel guilty enough to want to do it. You can't be busted for taking that stuff to the UK but it probably wouldn't go down well with everyone in your family, or the authorities, if they knew you had a hand in euthanising your old man. Am I right?"

"Er, spot on, I'd say. You have thought about this," I said.

"Thing is this, you have to live with your decision to take the stuff home, which may well be a moot point. You would have to live with him killing himself with your knowledge, and you can't share that with anyone." Chris surmised correctly. "I do not envy you."

"I'm back where I started," I said. "I was hoping one of the Customs posts we went through would take it away from me - shit! If we get it back, which is starting to look like a long shot I have to take it to him but hope that he doesn't use it."

"Thin, wouldn't you say?" said Chris.

"Very thin," I agreed. "More tea, vicar?" I offered the teapot to let us both off the hook of this conversation. I had no idea what to do about the Dogsbane. I could try to get some more. I could even fly back to the UAE while Chris waited in Egypt. I decided I would wait to see what happened when we returned to Cairo and then make a decision. It was a long shot and I was really fed up with my father at that point.

He was doing his damnedest to ruin my trip of a lifetime, which was interesting for someone who'd never really taken an interest in me at any other time.

We went to look at the island that held the Temple of Khnum. As the island was the main feature of the view from our window how could we not? Elephantine Island is the largest of the Aswan area islands, and is one of the oldest sites in Egypt, with artefacts dating to pre-dynastic periods. The reason for this is probably its location at the first Egyptian cataract, or rapid-like waterfall if you will, of the Nile, which provided a natural boundary between Egypt and Nubia (Sudan to you and me). As an island, it was also easy to defend. The ancient town located in the southern part of the island was also a fortress through much of its history.

Elephantine is Greek for elephant and a brand of kiddie's shoes. Large boulders in the river near the island resembled bathing elephants from afar on a hazy day with the wind in the right direction hence the island's name perhaps. I see no reason for the children's shoe link however.

The island is beautiful. One of its main attractions is its Nilometer, which is one of only three on the Nile. These measured the water level of the Nile as late as the nineteenth century. A kind of . . . if you can't see this it's really deep . . . type of thing.

Chris, apropos of nothing in particular, explained that, "Knitted socks, discovered in Ancient Egyptian tombs, were dated back as far as the third century AD."

It's nice that he is on the same planet at times even if not in the same timeframe.

With the temples and other ruins that Chris and I had seen plus the two days with Abdul Rahman in Luxor and Western Thebes we found we were suffering from an uncommon complaint. Temple overload started creeping in. This is a form of sensory overload. Something that would make you gasp in awe formerly is reduced to 'oh yeah' or 'that's nice'. Egypt has too much tangible history for anyone not to become a trifle blasé over time.

We took it easy for the rest of the day and as the sun dipped over the yardarm, it was time for a gin and tonic on the terrace of the hotel before dinner. We dined at a quieter restaurant without the Congo dancing, not as entertaining but surprisingly there are times when peace, tranquillity and a bottle or two of 'Nefertitti' wine, I believe it was called, is all that is required. Egyptian wine in 1991 was not the greatest, but it hit the spot. We turned in for the evening as we were going to move on tomorrow. Chris and I decided to leave the temples alone for a while and go and get wet in the Red Sea.

Chapter Eleven

With the temple overload and all, we thought a change of pace would be a good idea. We were to go diving soon but we had toyed with the idea of going to Abu Simbel. It was quite a drive and the flight prices were not friendly. After checking the availability of petrol or benzene on the road down there, we were reliably misinformed that it was difficult to come by. Not wanting to be stuck miles from anywhere in southern Egypt without petrol, surrounded by hoards of Nubians and Nile crocodiles practising running in zigzags, we took the cowardly option and decided to head straight for the East Coast for some more R&R, after all this was a vacation not a forced march.

Having since seen pictures of Abu Simbel I have to go there one day maybe when I come back to see Petra and the rest of Jordan, for now the thought of diving most definitely appealed.

Chris and I had two full sets of diving equipment in the back of the truck, even an emergency air tank, and we believed it was time to go somewhere to get wet, and Hurghada on the eastern Egyptian coast looked the best bet.

The petrol or gas stations outside of Cairo were interesting as the fuel was still hand-cranked into the tank at some of the places we visited and one buys benzene not gas or petrol.

Most people would make a joke about hand cranking, but not me. In most places, no prices were available and that's when a little negotiating could come into play. Being used to paying the prices on the pump, even in the UAE, it was a little nerve wracking buying benzene. Who knows what was being hand-cranked into the truck.

Different-ness is a big part of why one travels, that, and getting away from the mind-numbing tedium that dogs so many of us in our work lives. I had definitely barked up that tree once or twice. Getting ourselves to a road even less travelled by tourists than usual, we headed for the Red Sea.

We reached the coast in one piece and were separated from a couple more 'bitches' but hey it was worth it for the cultural interaction. As we'd reached the coast it meant we'd soon be getting down to some serious scuba diving. This was one area of the trip where we knew exactly what we wanted to be doing. Chris was relatively new to diving but already an avid fan. I already had many dives under my weight belt.

The Red Sea is many colours but not red, except that is, at certain times of the year when a certain little critter multiplies by gazillions to make what is known as an algal bloom. I studied this stuff at Southampton University on the South Coast of England when I wanted to be a marine scientist, so bear with me if I get a little excited at being able to use the expensive and hard-won knowledge I earned for once in my life. It will probably be the only time.

"Chris do you know why it is called the Red Sea?" I asked.

"I have a feeling you are going to tell me, oh master."

"At certain times of the year the blue algae *Trichodesmium erythraeum*, and try saying that while dancing a conga, dyes the tropical blue-green waters of the Red Sea a beautiful orangey-red. It's called a bloom," I said.

"Imagine how many of those little critters there have to be to change the colour of a sea," said Chris. He absorbs facts and doesn't mind where they come from.

"The marine world is amazing, and approximately seventy-one per cent of the planet Earth is under water. And, eighty-five per cent of all plant life is in that water." I was giving Chris some of his own medicine as this was one area where I did know a thing or two.

About 40 million years ago, give or take, the African and Arabian tectonic plates began to break and separate somewhat like a Kit-Kat, and this is still happening at the rate of about half an inch per year. As with most break-ups a rift occurs – this one is the Syrian-African Rift. The Syrians got the house and car, Africa got the kids and the boat.

The Syrian-African Rift is responsible for such geological treasures as the mountains of Sinai (so Moses should be thankful) the Dead Sea and the Jordan Valley. The reason I'm telling you about the rift is so that I can tell you about the testicle-shrivelling depths around these parts.

The waters surrounding the Sinai Peninsula are relatively shallow on the Suez side, about 100 metres, meaning that on air you are not going to see the bottom let alone touch it but it is diveable by humans. On the Gulf of Aqaba side, it reaches about 2,000 metres. Diveable by sperm whales but Emperor penguins would turn back at about 700 metres and

Weddell seals can dive to about 1,000 metres while Elephant seals go even further to 1,800. Humans can go safely, and without decompression diving, to about 50 metres maximum.

The south of the peninsula and the main body of the Red Sea is where it gets scarily deep, about 2,500 metres, too much for any but the most reckless sperm whales. This depth continues all the way down to the shallow exit into the Indian Ocean at the Bab el Mandab, which I'm sure you all know well. The rift is also the reason for the Rift Valley that glides south into tropical, deep, dark and mysterious Africa. I know a little about deep, dark Africans too, her name was Naima.

Cruising into Hurghada in our incredibly reliable, Nissan Pathfinder Chris and I found our way to an agreeable hostelry, the ingeniously named Gold Sands Hotel just before dark. It turned out to be something of a rip-off and we soon after moved to the Africa 2 at a third of the price thanks to some new friends. We would check out the scuba diving operation we had read about in our guidebook, Ocean Red Divers, in the morning.

Looking out to sea as the sun went down I regurgitated a line from the Ancient Mariner meant for such times as they'd never been any other use to me, "The sun's rim dips; the stars rush out: At one stride comes dark."

"With far-heard whisper, o'er the sea, off shot the spectre-bark," added Chris.

"Can't beat a classical education for useless information and apt quotes, eh, what!"

There were girls in bikinis in Hurghada! Might not be a big issue for most but we've just been living in the Middle East, in Abu Dhabi, without break for months and months; a place where a show of stocking is thought of as something shocking, but here heaven knows, maybe anything goes. I'm over egging the pudding but I was happy to be here.

Even now, one cannot help but notice anything of a slightly racy nature in the Middle East. However, you know, as a bachelor I hasten to add, that it's getting bad when you think things like Baywatch are worth watching. The whole female thing is so foreign that it is intriguing. Women swathed in black drift by in supermarkets and malls and I try not to look at absolutely anything they have on display such as eyes, hands or mouth. I can't help myself it makes me look. I am, like so many, very childish so tell me not to do something and that is exactly what I want to do.

In Hurghada the very next day after our arrival I'm staring at the girls in bikinis and dribbling. Thank goodness for dark glasses and napkins. I'll get over it soon enough.

Chris, without taking his eyes off a deeply tanned and pleasantly muscular girl with long black hair and a raucous laugh we know is called Sam, because we heard her friend call her that, says, "So, diving or sightseeing today?"

Starting to talk as I was pouring cold water into my mouth deposited water down my front and I decided that I really needed to go diving before I made a total idiot of myself. The damp bib on the front of my shirt will dry soon.

"I'd love to be able to stand up without giving too much away, so I'm furiously thinking about stripping the engine of the Nissan down, to take my mind off what it is on at the moment, just give me a minute and

I should be able to walk." I said. I felt stupid in truth, like one of those dogs who wants to shag your leg.

I rather like the look of Sam's friend whose name we don't know yet but who is slightly less tanned, taller and has a smoky voice and a laugh to match. The two girls are the focus of male attention and we figure immediately that they would not be interested in us. Chris and I both sighed at the same time - fools that we were. The people the girls are sitting with are what appear to be a small group of divers - tanned, young and fit, so I suck in my tummy, Chris doesn't need to (damn it) and we approach with our kit. I hold mine in front of me.

"Hey, guys," I say as casually as possible, "any chance of getting a dive today?"

"Maybe, mate, if the bloody Dive Master ever shows up. The instructor is here but he won't leave without a number two," says a jovial Kiwi called Peter and then looking up he added; "Here comes Mark now, he's the instructor I was telling you about."

You can spot a diving instructor from miles away especially a working one. Tanned, fit with cockiness to the stride. Mark has a friendly face too. "You guys looking for a dive?" says Mark. "I'm afraid my DM (Dive Master) has let me down today."

It was my chance to shine. It was perfect. My thousands of dollars in training and overactive sense of achieving would pay me back some for a change. "Is an MSDT any use to you," I said. (MSDT = Master Scuba Diver Trainer, a member of the Professional Association of Diving Instructors (PADI for short)). PADI meant 'Put Another Dollar In' for me. I didn't want to teach; I just had to be an instructor or not go diving. You know me well enough by now.

"You got ID?" Mark said with a little suspicion in his voice while his face conveyed relief.

I already had it out of my waterproof diver's wallet. You can sell me anything when I'm in the obsessed stage of achieving. "I'm a Medic First Aid Instructor too, name's Greg." We shook hands in a firm manly sort of way. I could tell he worked for a living and I was sure my hand would recover its feeling quite soon.

"What about him?" said Mark, indicating Chris with a nod.

With Mark's tacit acceptance, I had just risen to demi-god in the immediate social hierarchy. I was qualified to comment on Chris's scuba diving competence. "Advanced Open Water and solid," I said offering Chris as much of my newfound credibility as I could.

The girls Chris and I had been ogling had been listening to this interaction and I caught the eye of Sam's friend; she was smiling. I smiled back but I've never been good at that sort of thing and I know it didn't come across too well. I am better as a predator in one-to-one situations where I can bore a girl into submission. My voice can be quite hypnotic coupled with vast amounts of alcohol. When I force a smile, it often looks more like severe indigestion. Diving, concentrate on the diving. I don't have the tools to strip down the Nissan's engine but if I did . . . it works, you know . . . and it is a male secret for taking one's mind off something in hurry. You just do something manly and practical in your head to take your mind off of women or sex, but not beer, nothing takes your mind off beer especially when you've had a couple.

"Well, Greg," said Mark, "you're a life-saver. We've got two dives slated and if you DM for me yours are free."

I believe I said something like YEEESSSS! on the inside, but on the outside I said, "Fine with me, Mark, happy to help." I'd have been happy to DM and still pay so it was a good result.

We had an easy drift dive at about twenty to twenty-five metres along a coral reef first. A drift dive is where you drop in and down to the planned depth then let the current take you along. It can be a relaxing way to dive and if the DM tows a buoy, the boat driver can follow quite closely if necessary. If you plan it right, the boat picks you up when you have drifted far enough or you have reached your air limit. The dive was spectacular and I've found out that no one with us is higher qualified in diving than Chris, but everyone seems switched on, this makes for a much more relaxed DM.

As DM, I have to back up the instructor and watch for any problems. I dive at the rear and watch the divers and the leader for any signs of distress or difficulty. It was easy money and Chris and I split the benefit. I knew he would do the same; we are working quite well together as a travelling team so far and that is no small benefit. We had agreed that we would spend whatever we wanted on food, accommodation and general expenses and then split it all out 50:50 once back in England.

The second dive, after a rest and a pleasant lunch of rice and vegetables on the boat; is to a large collection of coral with amazing colours. Colour disappears so quickly in the sea. The deeper you go the fewer colours are apparent. I won't go into the physics of it but you will be able to work it out if I tell you that the sequence in which these colours disappear is red, orange, yellow, green and blue. This is why many divers carry a torch because then you can see the real colour of something even at depth. If you cut one of the less experienced divers with your big rusty manly diver's knife, at 20 metres for example, his blood comes out green and attracts every meat-eater for miles.

Mark and I worked well together and everyone got back safe with plenty of air and all their limbs intact – no bends or Nitrogen Narcosis.

The sea is crystal clear and is always a shock for Britons used to diving in that country's murky depths. They look into the water and scream "Fish! Coral! The bottom! Oh my God, THE BOTTOM!" Sweet really, because divers who learn in tropical waters, don't scream "murky water" when we go to Britain we just don't go diving – it's too cold– I'm a big wimp where the cold is concerned.

Good instructors get a great deal of respect and as you have to trust them with your life, they deserve it in most cases. I had done the minimum instructing to get my qualifications. I only wanted the certificate; I didn't want to do it for a living. Mark on the other hand was a thorough professional and definitely doing it for a living. I liked him a lot and showed him respect in front of the others too so there was no doubt who was boss.

On the boat back everyone was happy, excited at two good dives and swapping stories about what they'd seen and so on. The biggest thing we'd seen was some Napoleon Wrasse but nowhere near as big as I've heard they can be. The excited chatting is an important part of diving and all that information goes into one's dive log so that when the diver turns up at another dive site or diving organisation the instructor or DM can tell at a glance what type of experience the diver has had. Your diving partner, DM or dive leader signs the log.

"So, Peter, what's this about a Great White Shark in your log?" I said.

"There were hundreds of the buggers, mate," said Peter. Not rising to the bait.

"And that was Moby Dick that went past, I suppose."

"Even here, it's too cold to see anybody's dick, mate." He wiggled his little finger for everyone to see and laugh at. Diving is often not the glamorous sport people imagine it to be. Try talking normally to another person while they have a huge gob of snot stuck to the side of their face, it's off-putting.

It was a good day's diving. Neither a temple nor hieroglyph in sight. The people we dived with while we were in Hurghada were a good bunch, younger than Chris and me but not by enough to make it an issue. One was a Royal Marine officer cadet having his big holiday before he joined his unit, one was a writer for a travel magazine, who kept disappearing to go and review a hotel or a restaurant, and the requisite smattering of antipodeans. They were all keen to get as much diving done as they could while they were in one of the three top diving destinations in the world.

When we weary scuba diving warriors returned to port, the girls were still hanging around. We were all still high on the dives and no one wanted it to end. Sam and her friend suggest we all go for drinks and dinner. Chris and I looked at one another in disbelief because unless we were both crazy the girls seemed interested in us. Remove the air filter and loosen the nuts around the carburettor, make sure that the battery is disconnected, take out the spark plugs . . .

Drinks were numerous and the Egyptian pizza wasn't too bad either. Sam and Helen, now we knew her name, were hilarious, good fun. They thought our trip sounded fantastic but teased us mercilessly about staying in five-star hotels and not roughing it. They were interested in us. Over the next few days, Sam, Chris, Helen, and I became close. We even moved to another hotel that was cheaper and closer to where they were staying. The things one does for a smile and flutter of eyelashes and the hope of more, of course.

We continued to dive every day. The dives were stunning but we still hadn't had any close encounters with anything big or mean.

Treating the coral reefs appallingly, as the boat owners were, was a great sadness for me. Dive boats would anchor to them, which is bad enough, but instead of lifting the anchor carefully, would pull away a section of the reef killing it.

Coral is a living being with an exoskeleton and a delicate mucus membrane around that, touching it with your finger can kill. A piece of coral someone wants to take home for their mantelpiece may have taken hundreds of years to grow. Look at it, wonder at it but don't touch it. Your dive leader, if he or she is any good, will point out the dead stuff you can take home. I get quite evangelical about this as you can tell. I make no apologies. Here endeth the lesson.

After talking, Chris and I decided that we had had enough of Hurghada but something was keeping us here, actually two 'somethings'. The chance encounter with Sam and Helen and then getting together with them was too good to give up yet. We decided to ask them if they wanted to come to Sinai with us and see whether all the flirting, attraction and need for mental car repairs were mutual. I popped the question over a beer.

"Helen, Chris and I had been thinking about going over to Sinai to look around and dive," I said a little sheepishly. "Is that something you and Sam would be interested in?"

"Don't be a wanker, Greg, you must know I like you, and Chris and Sam are getting on OK, of course we want to come with you, do you have room in the truck with all your paraphernalia, darling?" she said. Her dark sultry voice made my pulse quicken, but my blood pressure must have gone through the roof when she leaned closer and said, "And another thing, don't you think you've waited long enough to make your move on me?"

So, well then, and off we go! Repacking the car was a challenge to accommodate two more people but we managed. I had offered to strap Chris to the roof but it wasn't necessary.

I have no idea what we'd done to deserve such good fortune but I wasn't about to complain.

Travelling to Sinai, we planned to overnight in the desert, sleep under the stars and the girls were going to cook us a curry on an open fire. We stocked up on the necessities which included numerous bottles of rosé Nefertiti, the only drinkable Egyptian wine we had found so far.

Driving up the Red Sea coast road was interesting too especially as we were approaching Suez. We saw our first Aircraft Carrier, not that we were really searching for them, and Chris excelled with his knowledge of warships.

"The launching mechanism of a carrier ship that helps planes to take off could throw the Nissan over a mile," he said.

"I dunno Chris," I said trying to make a funny off his comment, "it would save a little on petrol I guess, but the landing bothers me."

The back streets of Suez were depressing – industrialisation and poverty doesn't look too good anywhere, but mixed together they are particularly obnoxious. Here again we see the mixture of ancient and modern as in Cairo; donkey and carts, trucks, smart businessmen and shoeless kids looking to make ends meet. Every time we slowed down for a corner, to check our map, or ask for directions, kids swarmed around crying, "Baksheesh, baksheesh," some of them looked in a bad way, but what can you do? We buckled and gave coins and a few notes away to the ones who look like they wouldn't survive without it. The dust, poverty and the heat make Suez a particularly oppressive yet great place to leave.

Back on the Sinai Peninsula we found our way back to the road we used last time to drive past the dykes and St Katherine's but this time we could have more fun with it as we knew what was in store. What we wouldn't have given for a top-notch map like the Ordnance Survey Maps one can get in Britain. We got by with what we had. Sam and Helen had never done desert driving before yet showed no fear or reserve in their enjoyment. As late afternoon approached, we turned off into the desert to look for a place to camp. We got right away from the road but avoided any sand that looked too soft or too deep. Interestingly that's not what we should have been looking for but our efforts took us right away from the road and into a sheltered area by a rocky outcrop – perfect. We set up camp.

There will be moments in your life that will never leave you, some will be bad and some will be good. Either way, recalling these moments for me brings a tear to my eye. After being industrious and helping to set up our camp I turned and looked straight into one of those moments. The sunset, on that day, on Sinai, was truly spectacular. Chris took a photograph that could never do it justice but we all understood his sentiment. Then he got out his notebook.

"Fifty years ago there were Cheetahs on the Sinai, so many that the Bedu would wear their skins" – presumably once the cheetahs had finished with them," he said.

As the sun went down there was a noticeable cooling but not the freezing many talk about in the deserts at night. Even a pleasant breeze wasn't enough to shake us from the awe-inspiring sight that was our sky. With no light coming from anywhere and just the wide-open expanse of the Egyptian night sky, it looked almost grey with stars. With so many visible, the view is humbling. Shooting stars flew across the sky every few seconds it seemed. It was time for another of Chris's hidden talents; this guy never ceased to amaze me – stories around the campfire.

A natural lull in the chatter and bonhomie left Chris an opening for the story he got from an old Egyptian guy he got talking to in Hurghada: "You know where we are is steeped in some pretty scary history. Less than a hundred years ago, during a time when the Sinai was suffering from a severe drought, and in order for the people in Nuweiba to eat, they had to go west to the British in Suez for food, and that sometimes meant passing Jebel Barka, just over the hill, where the Cave of the Ghouls is."

No one laughed at the story; we all smiled and waited for the rest of it eagerly.

"On top of Jebel Barka lived a family of ghouls who were in the habit of eating passers-by." He paused and looked around; Helen and Sam were lapping the story telling up. "Well, one night five men went to Suez via Jebel Barka and one was left behind only to be found by a beautiful lady ghoul who gave him a choice - sex or be eaten."

I swear Sam licked her lips. Chris had changed the tempo somewhat with a cheeky smile added: "The guy did what any red-blooded male would do in that situation."

The girls share a look between them and Helen says,"What's that then, he went out with the lads, got drunk and then tried to screw next door's cat."

Chris had become the serious storyteller again: "A year later the lady ghoul saw the man again and informed him he had a daughter, whom he then took into his home."

Another pause for effect, it was time for Chris to pay homage to Nefertiti.

"All was well until years later when the father passed a desecrated grave," explained Chris in a matter-of-fact kind of way. "The girl's new husband knew of her history and after being told of the incident, followed his wife one night to a grave where she ate another dead person. He was horrified of course but what could he do? Well, he had recently purchased several huge sacks of food, so while she slept, he pushed all the goods over onto her and she was killed. In true Arabic fashion," said Chris finishing with a flourish and referring to the way women have often been treated in the Middle East.

The girls protested at the ending but Chris responded with, "It was listed as an accident," and laughed.

A natural lull occurred in the conversation and everyone seemed to be making contented noises and sighs. "More wine anyone," I said proffering the bottle. "And I hope no one is thinking of having sex with ghoulish beings tonight." Helen looked at me, smiled and made a scary face. I felt Nefertiti reaching warm and pleasant places; I hoped she wouldn't be alone in that quest.

The story had pretty much brought the evening to a close. We finished off another bottle of wine and started settling down for the night. Chris had put the tent up but no one could leave the sight of the stars. With the arms of Nefertiti around me, and Helen close by, I doze and drift in and out of a light sleep.

Very soon after drifting off, I wake to the sound of heated voices. Helen was in my arms which was a development but Sam and Chris were having a row. To cut a long story short Sam and Chris wanted to get intimate but Chris was still hung up on and old girlfriend who ditched him for his best friend and every time he and Sam were getting close he started talking about her in some kind of weird reflex. Sam was no wallflower and she was letting Chris have it.

Fully awake again, Helen and I decide to open another bottle of wine and as we've had the dinner, we may as well watch the show. The curry, made by the girls was awful and you are the first person I've shared that with so keep it to yourself. We eat it in any event, as the wine helped no end. Sam and Chris quiet down and lay separately on the mats. Helen and I decide to take a stroll.

While we're strolling hand in hand, let me tell you how stupid we had been going off road into the desert in the Sinai without any guidance or planning. Fortunately, we didn't find any of this out until much later but what we should have been looking for instead of a great Ordnance Survey Map was a great map of ordnance. Helen and I were playing a particularly nasty form of Russian roulette. The Sinai in 1991, and even today has millions of landmines all over it. Some of these mines just maim, some of them kill and many of them are booby-trapped.

About 20 per cent of the world's 'unexploded' landmines are in Egypt. The problem in many cases seems to be that its land mines are old and hard to locate and whose design is for use against tanks, whereas international criticism and therefore monetary donations to clear them focuses on anti-personnel mines.

With thousands injured and an adverse effect on the country's economy, mines are a problem. Egypt and Israel dumped about six million mines in the Sinai between 1967 and 1973. The land where they lay, great swathes where only fools and camels wander, earns the title 'The Devil's Garden' by the local population.

Because these mines have been in the ground for so long military analysts say that inclement weather may have increased the depth at which many land mines lay by as much as eight metres. This, unfortunately, rules out the use of normal mine-detection methods. Additionally, the corroded trigger mechanisms on many of these hideous contraptions are unstable. Mines intended for the hefty bulk of a tank could detonate from the weight of a cheetah, should any exist, or even a couple making out.

Some mines explode by themselves. The Bedu have had many killed as has the Egyptian military and of course another source of mine fodder is tourists getting off the beaten track. People die or are maimed every year. Clearing millions of mines still leaves millions more.

Helen and I were oblivious to many things during our stroll but we had no idea about landmines and that every step we took could have been potentially fatal. The earth moved anyway.

Morning came early and Chris and Sam were already up and making breakfast, their argument apparently forgotten. We wanted to get to Sharm-el-Sheikh that day to set up camp, check out the dive operations and then get to Nuweiba to renew our two-week pass. We knew we could just wing it and bribe someone in Alexandria when we caught the ferry for Crete but we thought we'd try to do the right thing especially as we had friends in Nuweiba now, big friends in large leather jackets.

We looked for booze in Dahab, and somewhere to stay the night, but therewas a clamp-down on alcohol in the whole Dahab region, and would we like to buy some dope, LSD, cocaine, grass or Heroin? We politely decline all the class 'A' drugs offered by the 60's rejects in flowery shirts, this is not that sort of trip, man. We leave Dahab, because Sam has a thirst that water apparently cannot quench, to spend the night in Nuweiba before heading on down to Sharm el-Sheikh.

Chapter Twelve

We let the girls book us into a 'hotel' and I use that word advisedly. It was the worst hovel in which I'd ever spent the night. The girls had to stay in separate rooms from us as the owner is a good Muslim and he knows we are not married.

I have never roughed it in a place like this before and personally would have rather gone and lain on the local garbage tip. It was disgusting. There was a two-inch gap under the door to our room; the so-called clean sheets that we requested had all manner of stains on them. I didn't want to guess. And, I really, really didn't want Chris's opinion.

I decided to sleep in my clothes as my sleeping bag and a few other useful cold weather bits and pieces were en route to England. I could not bring myself to touch the sheets and if it weren't for the unmerciful ragging we'd have got from the girls, Chris and I would have already been in the Nissan heading for another hotel.

Fifteen Egyptian pounds a night to sleep in a bed that moves before you get into it and Sam and Helen insist the manager is gouging.

"Maybe all the wildlife in the bed, shower and room are extras," I offered.

"The toilet doesn't work, the shower is only operable if you sit on the toilet and barely has enough water pressure to make it out of the showerhead." Chris investigated the shower even further and wished he hadn't. "I think we should call David Attenborough," he added. "There are species of animal in this toilet cum-shower-room that were supposed to be extinct."

Turning on the tap brings forth the plumbing's rendition of the 1812 Overture and gobs of brownish-black water. It was my turn to express disgust as the plumbing is laughably out of tune.

"We are paying for this . . . are we mad." My voice was hitting notes it hadn't since prior to puberty. I looked at Chris and we knew that we couldn't leave as it wouldn't have been fair to the girls who were on a tight budget. "There is only one way to get through this," I announced, "and that is with large amounts of our favoured beverage."

We got ready to go to another hotel with the girls, the Barracuda, for a beer and they only had two in the whole place. We drank those, four bottles of wine and bought all of the rosé Nefertiti they had left – a paltry four bottles. Without giving the drink-driving situation a thought, we then drove off into the desert to dodge mines, have piggyback fights and generally behave like kids. We left the truck engine running so that we could blast the stereo, we laid the mats out and then it was Chris and Sam's turn to go for a stroll and hopefully they wouldn't blow up this time either figuratively or literally.

Helen and I were fooling around on the mat when I felt something on my toe. Now I was mentally engaged in what I was doing with Helen so I tried to ignore the itchy feeling on my toe and continue exploring Mount St Helen. The itching did not go away; in fact, it was not really an itching anymore but still an annoyance. I reached down to brush off whatever little critter thought it could have its way with me and picked up a six-inch black scorpion by its tail between my thumb and forefinger. Still distracted I brought it close to my face in the half-light provided by the truck . . .

The language I'll leave to your imagination but a rainbow has fewer colours. I threw the beast down on the mat screaming like a little girl and Helen, without looking, brushed it off the mat and under the Nissan.

I said, "Helen that was a bloody scorpion."

She said, "Don't be ridiculous you don't get scorpions that big . . . do you?"

Chris and Sam came back because of all the noise and didn't believe my story. Helen wasn't sure so you have to take my word for it – trust me – it was a scorpion and a bloody great big one. I have since seen them that big in my old villa in the desert. With the mood lost and Nefertiti having deserted us, we went back to the hotel. Chris and I had to get ready for our renewal, which sounds almost religious.

Unfortunately, for us, our friend in the black leather jacket was not there. We hid the truck in the streets of Nuweiba and took our reams of paperwork with us. We knew we could stay; we were just not sure about the Nissan. Ali was there and he remembered us. We had to go see the guy who was beaten up by the leather jacket last time, he was not there either – a conspiracy. This guy was on holiday and he's been replaced by his belligerent brother in arms. We were prepared.

The new official would only say no. We kept saying yes and so it went. We showed him bits of paper from before, we made logical arguments and then Chris had the best idea of all. I don't know why neither of us thought of it earlier – get Ali to explain what had happened before. Chris went to find him while I stared at this guy and tried to think of all the things I could do that would annoy or shame him into extending our pass. Fortunately, for me, I managed to keep my mouth shut.

Chris returned smiling and said, "Ali is on his way."

"Ali Bombaye, Ali Bombaye" I chanted.

I bet the Customs Nazi couldn't figure why we were so pleased when Ali came trundling in the room with tea for everyone and went about explaining everything we had, but in the right way. Where we were confident or even arrogant, he was deferring and obsequious, where we were loud and aggressive he was calm and placid. I imagine he told this chap about the man mountain in the leather jacket too. Whatever else he said it was enough. The new official wrote 'extended' in Arabic at the request of the man mountain so that he couldn't be to blame for anything and let us go.

The girls had been checking out Nuweiba and couldn't wait to leave.

We headed for Sharm and asked the girls to check out the hotels because they had done such a great job in Nuweiba. Sam, at that point said something about going forth and multiplying, it went over my head. What they didn't know was that wewere checking into the Hilton to treat them, but whatever they found out would be useful for afterwards.

As we didn't know where to find them we had them checking the Hilton reception every two hours – we just missed them after Chris and I had finished changing money, posting letters and all the other little domestic things one has to do on an extended trip, so Chris and I had tea and took stock of our financial situation. We were spending faster than we thought we would but we also weren't really showing any restraint. Once the girls were gone, we would start some sort of a budget. Europe would eat us alive if we continued at the rate we were going at.

The girls ragged us for checking in to another five-star hotel but quietened down when they saw the suite. I don't recall them saying anything else untoward after that.

Looking briefly at the hotel and the surrounding area we were much happier than we had been in Nuweiba. Sharm el Sheikh seemed like a nice place and it made us think we should both call our families, so we did, even at hotel rates. No news for me but Chris had become an uncle for the first time. Something to celebrate

We had to meet up with some friends in the Sanafia Hotel. Sven our Swedish diving instructor friend from Dubai was there with his partner David. Sam and Helen loved Sven and David instantly especially David because he was so camp. David apparently was looking forward to going down with us in the morning. Sven has taught David to dive and they have booked up some diving for all of us with a highly reputable outfit recommended by all the other instructors from the UAE.

The Sanafia Hotel, the Divers' Den, at that time was THE place for divers to hang out in the evening. Low, Arabic style cushioned chairs, incense, Egyptian Stella and The Doors playing in the background – heaven, and just the place to try to exercise the hangover that had been dogging us all day. We drank to Chris becoming an uncle.

Foolishly, I drank too much again knowing that I would have to dive in the morning. This is one of the things we instructors teach as a no-no, for good reason. On the first dive, I blow chunks, as its known, through my regulator. That made the fish happy because they got my breakfast but it is not good form for an instructor to be doing that in front of less experienced divers, but it's nothing compared to what was about to happen as I tried to make up for my puking.

Making a show of feeding the fish is a beginner's mistake. Diving deeper than the plan, because of something shiny, is brainless. I saw something shiny and went from about 25 metres to a little more than 40, right at the edge of what my PADI diving tables recommended. The shiny thing was forgotten, as I got 'narked'.

In police TV shows getting narked is having someone give you up to the authorities, in diving parlance it means being under the influence of Nitrogen Narcosis and even though the affected individual may seem to be having the time of his life he is, in fact, in great danger. Luckily, Sven noticed and dived towards me holding up two fingers. I held up two fingers too, which was not the response he was looking for and it meant I really could be in trouble if he didn't help me ascend.

Nitrogen narcosis, 'the martini effect' or more poetically, the 'raptures of the deep' is the direct toxic effect of high nitrogen pressure on nerve conduction. It could happen at 20 metres or not at 40 metres plus, it varies from person to person from day to day. It is an alcohol-like effect. Compared to rapidly drinking martinis on an empty stomach it sounds like fun. The more depth after onset; the more martinis one seems to be drinking. The result is hopefully just being a little shaken and not too stirred. In The Silent World the greatest diver of them all, Jacques Cousteau, admits to enjoy being 'narked' but rightly being scared of it, he wrote:

'I am personally quite receptive to nitrogen rapture. I like it and fear it like doom. It destroys the instinct of life. Tough individuals are not overcome as soon as neurasthenic persons like me, but they have difficulty extricating themselves. Intellectuals get drunk early and suffer acute attacks on all the senses, which demand hard fighting to overcome. When they have beaten the foe, they recover quickly. The agreeable glow of depth rapture resembles the giggle-party jags of the nineteen-twenties when flappers and sheiks convened to sniff nitrogen protoxide.'

This was the first time having raptures of the deep in almost 500 dives, but all the clues were there to see. I was not that fit at the time, I was drinking the night before diving, I had been drinking heavily in the days before the dive, I had not been getting enough sleep, I hadn't even been drinking enough water. Had I been conducting an experiment on whether I could contrive getting Nitrogen narcosis it would have read something like this paragraph.

My unfailing good luck bailed me out again as Sven came towards me holding up two fingers in the victory sign. If I hadn't been lit-to-the-gills I would have held up three fingers to acknowledge that I had seen his two, understood, and held up one more than him because I was alert.

Instead of doing what was required of me, I turned my two-finger reply into a rude gesture, which I found so funny I spat my regulator out – no more air for me. It is things like this that could lead to a diver's death, being narked is not being in control of oneself and when you are scuba diving, it is one place where you need to be in control. Divers suffering this condition have tried to share their regulators with the other occupants of the deep. Fish not having an overdeveloped sense of humour don't really find it that funny, but it is always surprising and new to them.

Sven in his consummate professional way took me by the arm and jollied me upward, as one does with a happy drunk, and popped my breathing apparatus back in my mouth. Inside a few seconds I was fully aware what I had been doing but could not for the life of me tell you why. The raptures disappear as quickly as they arrive and leave no after-effect, unlike a couple of bottles of Nefertiti or Martini for that matter.

Most of the other divers didn't know what had been going on until after the dive. On the whole a pretty dreadful one for me; throwing up through my regulator and then getting narked, well at least I'd got all of that out of my system, right.

The following day, promised a shark, we took the boat to Ras Mohammed early. Anchoring up in about 12 metres of water Sven, Chris and I were the first over the edge of the boat with directions where to go. A partial drift dive took us to the edge of a reef and we would hang out there until we were low on air and then we'd surface and the boat would pick us up. The drift was fun and we were checking out the reef. The colours of the coral were endless and it teemed with life. Sven showed Chris how to be exfoliated by a cleaner fish at a cleaner station. If you wait your turn at the appropriate places on a coral reef a fish will come up to you and literally start picking bits of dead skin and so on off of any exposed areas. This symbiotic experience is amazing to watch and uncanny to experience. Of course, it's not meant for humans but that has never stopped us interfering with nature before.

I am 'hovering' a little way from Sven and Chris. Effortlessly I became part of a shoal of thousands of 'Jacks'. What a calming sensation it was to be part of the shoal, looking around me, above me and below me there were nothing but other members of the shoal. I drifted, they drifted and then they parted and there about as large as me in length was a black-tipped reef shark cruising for food.

The shark was about five metres from me and I was about 30 metres down in mid water. If it had wanted me I had no chance, fortunately these fish are not interested in humans as we are too big and noisy, even if we do taste like chicken.

The shark's pilot fish led him about by his nose. It reminded me of a tail wagging a dog. The Jacks rather than being afraid of the shark brushed up against its tail for some reason. I was awestruck and felt privileged to experience such a wonder.

Sven had seen the shark and Chris was still at the cleaner station so both Sven and I were making as many noises as we could to attract Chris's attention. Finally, he looked round as a marine Porsche cruised right by him, no more than a few metres away. His eyes filled his face-mask and Sven moved to a position to catch him if he bolted for the surface, he didn't.

As the shark disappeared into the distance another member of the shark family, the Manta Ray treated us to a flying display. The Manta has to be the most elegant fish in the sea. It swam up the reef in front of us, made a sweeping 'aquabatic' turn, something the Red Arrows would have been proud of, if they could get their jets to fly underwater, and went back up the reef in its glide for food.

Back on the surface, everyone listened to our story of the shark. Sadly fewer and fewer sharks are being seen in the Red Sea as more and more humans arrive. The detrimental effect humans are having on the seas is catastrophic. Cousteau documented a prime example of this not that long before he died. He showed a dive site he visited in the 1960s lush with vegetation and teeming with life. Twenty-five years later the same site looked like the surface of the moon. Divers I hasten to add do not cause this damage but man's ever growing appetite for where to dump it's waste. It's a disgrace the way the sea becomes the dump for everything from radioactive waste, biological waste to everyday household waste. Well, the payback to humanity will be a bitch and I don't mean a pen. If you think that is a long way off and nothing to worry about there are prime examples of such toxic effect already on the surface, such as Minimata Bay, Japan. No more soapbox from me, check it out if you wish. You'll never eat sushi again.

So, dumping in the sea is bad and getting worse every day, diving and crusading, soapbox-standing diving instructors are good. Of course our rather intellectual car bumper stickers will just tell you that we'd rather be diving – don't let that fool you. What the stickers don't tell you is that we have to dive now, as there won't be anything left to see if we keep polluting the oceans, seas, lakes and rivers. It is a privilege to be able to swim with the fishes as long as it isn't under order of Don Corleone.

We were lucky to see our shark as no one else, that we knew of, in Sharm saw one while we were there. This of course gave us something to 'dine out on'. Among the wannabe fish at the 'Divers' Den' that week, we were the only ones with a close encounter of the Jaws kind.

We had eased up on our drinking after my rapturous misadventure and were getting serious about our diving. While we dived, the girls were getting serious suntans and talking about their last day, which was fast approaching. The new hotel we had moved to was a little like Fawlty Towers Egyptian style. I got the feeling perhaps we weren't tipping enough for room service around the time a few strange things started to happen. The room service telephone number changed four times in three days, then we started getting power outages, then the water was becoming very unreliable. Then Sven ordered an apple from room service and it came with teeth marks in it.

One afternoon when I called the latest number for room service I was told clearly that, "Room service is cancelled. We are a three-star hotel, we don't have to offer room service, but, we would like to, but we won't. Try again tomorrow." I was too flabbergasted to answer I just put the phone down, told Chris and we fell about. We were used to Egypt by now and we would leave the hotel soon enough.

The last dive of note was also to Ras Mohammed, but it is worthy of mention for another act of stupidity on my part aided and abetted by Sven and David this time. It's now I tell you that their names have been changed to protect them because they might get in a lot of trouble for what I'm about to tell you.

It was a nothing dive in the morning, quite shallow and lacking in anything of note other than the usual stunning coral with bright and gaily coloured fish by the million. Snorkelling after lunch until the second dive was always good relaxed fun and we were getting quite some interest from the local fish population who were obviously well clued in to getting food from humans. It's simply that one or two of them had little concept of size; white meant egg and that was that.

One of the divers on the boat was toting some serious camera equipment including a professional white strobe flash on the end of a rod attached to his camera. He held the rod to steady the camera. We got into the water and as the fish arrived, he began to take pictures. What he didn't see was the large Napoleon Wrasse, a sizeable yet quite comical looking fish that keeps one fin tucked in its waistcoat like its namesake, approaching from behind. It was about the size of a Volkswagen Beetle. The Napolean Wrasse saw his white strobe flash and its ganglion of nerves that passes for a brain sent the message to the rest of its body, 'egg'.

Napoleon Wrasse do not eat humans but they are partial to hard-boiled eggs. In a flash, if you will, the strobe, its rod, the photographer's hand and half of his forearm disappeared into the Napoleon's gaping maw. David Attenborough, Shark Gordon or someone clever in these matters would probably say the worst thing that you could do in this situation would be to pull your arm away. Meanwhile the terror-struck photographer's brain was crying run, climb a wall, sit in a tree, pooh your pants, just get your arm out of this animal's mouth. A frenzied yank and we saw the green of his blood.

Napoleon Wrasse do not eat humans but they do have rough barbs on the inside of their mouths for their other food groups such as pasta and figs.

The diver's arm was not a pretty sight and we had to help him out of the water. His diving holiday was over. He would be OK and there would be little or no scarring but he wouldn't be able to dive for quite some time. It was a funny thing to see this huge fish trying to eat the strobe flash along with the diver's arm but the injury was not funny. It did spit him out quite quickly and we, including the one-armed photographer, were enticing them with food to come closer for better photographs so we were to blame.

In the afternoon Sven, David and I, went for a dive and we were going to go deep for the hell of it; Chris was minding his untameable bowels that had kept him out of the water for a couple of days.

It was all brainless macho stuff and I can't believe now I did it. By the end of the dive, my tank emptied while we were on our third decompression stop. Another 'nothing much' dive became a competition to see who could go the deepest. It was so stupid and just like boys. We hit fifty metres and someone went to fifty-five, stupidly the next one would go to sixty and so on. Finally, with all our testosterone expended we held our dive computers together at seventy-eight and a half metres – just a tad off the PADI diving scales. It was the bottom as far as we were concerned but we could see over the edge to the drop off; it just went dark. We had to surface and carefully. We knew our dive computers would tell us what deco stops to do on the way up but no one considered that we might run out of air. A sudden necessity to surface could mean the bends and maybe even death if a decompression chamber was not to hand.

On the last 'deco stop', after I had signalled a couple of times that I was low on air, my air gave out and we had three more minutes to complete decompressing according to my computer. It probably would have been fine to ignore the computer but I guess my sanity had returned and taking any more chances was not really a good idea. As I signalled the drawing of my hand across my throat gesture, meaning I was out of air, David passed me his alternate air source, called an Octopus; I was now sharing his air tank and sucking down air he may need. If that ran out that was it. We looked at his gauges and realised it would be close. Sven was also on vapours.

We made it. Breaking our kit down on the boat after a tense time, we were feeling foolish. Two instructors and a friend could have become statistics that day. We had to hope that no one would scroll through our dive computers to see how deep we had been because someone would not be able to resist asking questions.

When taking one's kit apart usually the hissing of air occurs as people use the force of the air to clean the all-important O-seals and other bits of equipment. When I took my kit apart, there was barely even a 'phut'. Enough diving, I was a danger to myself as well as others. Only sensible stuff from then on, well, mostly sensible. For now, it was time to get back to the shore, plan a leaving party for the girls, and arrange to meet up with them in London.

Seeing the girls off on their coach to Cairo airport, we offered to drive them but they wanted to sleep after their last night with us that entailed little sleep and lots of Nefertiti. We were sad to see them go but it was time for Chris and I to get on with our adventure and girls would get in the way. We had to get to Cairo a few days later for Chris's thirtieth birthday, and check the Dogsbane situation.

At that point we didn't realise we would be leaving Sharm as fugitives from the law.

Chapter Thirteen

After checking out from our wonderful hotel, which by the time we had left had no room service, no water and no electricity, we wondered what we would spend the discount on, upon which we had insisted and received. The obvious was Benzene; we repacked to accommodate Sven and David and headed for the local station.

After filling the Nissan's tank the attendant tried to charge us quite a bit more for the gas than the pump price. We took this to be the usual shakedown and refused. That went on for a few minutes and we got bored. I gunned the truck's engine, the attendant refused to take the money we offered, which matched that shown on the pump. Chris put the money on the top of the pump and got in the truck. I gunned the engine once more and the attendant stood in front of the truck. The sum of money we were arguing about was not a lot, but there would be no ripping off today.

I said to Chris, "What do you reckon?"

Chris said, "He'll move."

I eased the truck forward, the guy backed up, I kept easing forward and it got to the point where it was time for someone to blink, the attendant blinked and thank goodness as I was about to give in. We drove off. With the testosterone level at maximum, we all whooped and hollered like football hooligans. I'm sure our families would have been so proud of us.

We stopped off for lunch in a backstreet restaurant and then dropped into the dive centre before we hit the road. The boss saw us come in and sidled up to the truck. "You better not stick around, guys, the police were just here looking for you. Did you try and run down the gas station attendant?"

"It's a slightly longer story than that, he was trying to rip us off," I said.

"I would get going if I were you," said the dive centre boss. "They tend to fill cells and ask questions later around here."

We hit the road as fugitives from the law, the hole-in-the-brain gang.

Chris said, "Shit! I wonder if they took our number plate down."

"They must have, how else did they track us down to the dive centre so quickly?" I said.

"Sweetie," said David. "I wouldn't fret too much. They probably tracked us from being four white people in a big truck with tyres chained to the roof. It is rather an unusual sight."

"I hope you're right, David," I said. "I don't fancy spending any time in an Egyptian jail thank you very much."

"I don't know, darling," said David. "It might be fun."

"Don't be such a tart," said Sven.

We took the long way around Sinai to Cairo, as it was quicker. As you can see, we were used to navigating our way around Egypt by that point. We even found our way to the hotel in Cairo quite easily. Sven and David had booked themselves into a more modest pension not far from where we were staying.

We'd booked a suite at a five-star hotel, another Sheraton, of course (had to build up those miles). Sven and David were going to join us for a couple of days before we headed off for an ice-cold beer in Alexandria to jump on a ferry to Crete, which according to our research left every day.

Checking in, the receptionist passed on messages for us. There were cards and mail and so on but the biggest shock came in a Sheraton envelope. Shave my head and call me baldy if they hadn't found the Dogsbane. It was being kept in a walk-in fridge and all I had to do was show the duty manager this note and it would be returned to me. I caught my breath and my heart raced.

Chris saw the look on my face and said, "So they found it huh? You can start sweating about what to do with it again now."

"Yeah! Thanks for reminding me."

We walked through the door to the suite. Decorated beautifully, it was spacious but only had a double bed. I was prepared with the booking form Jeeta got for me before leaving Abu Dhabi. It clearly requested twin beds.

"We need another bed," I said calmly. You could almost hear the whoosh as the comment went over the bellhop's head. So used to everyone speaking English as well as numerous other languages an Arabic only speaker was a shock to the system. "Tefam Ingleesi?" (Do you speak English?) I asked. "La" was the brief reply. I called Reception and explained our situation to the English-speaking receptionist. His English wasn't that great either and tempers, including mine, were starting to fray. I put the telephone receiver down forcefully.

We need twin beds in our suite, so we need another bed." I was being 'yessed' quite a bit so I knew it was not getting through and just before tossing my toys around as one does when one is frustrated, with veins a-popping I shouted at the bellhop, "We need another bed."

The bellhop offered to unpack our bags but the withering looks he received had him scooting out of the door quite quickly. He was back in a couple of minutes beaming an as-yet-unnoticed crooked and nicotine-stained toothy grin as a guy from room service followed him in and lay a tray on the ornate coffee table. He removed the napkin with a flourish to show a setting for two people and a large basket of bread. "You need a bread," he offered.

Chris was already laughing and it took me a couple of seconds to catch up. Chris was rolling on the oversized double bed. The bellhop and the room service person were totally bemused. They talked, in Arabic, amongst themselves.

"They must be hungry from a long journey but why they don't want the bread anymore. It doesn't make sense, does it, Abdul."

"Don't piss in my ear and tell me its raining, Hakim. Let's toss the infidels off the balcony. Wait a minute the mouthy one wants to spell it out for us; he'll be demanding the manager next."

I started to explain, "We asked for a bed not bread," but it didn't go anywhere.

After a while, I asked for the duty manager to come to our room. Blow me down if it wasn't Fester from the Adams family. A baldhead and dark, dark rings around his eyes, I could not keep a straight face, and was terrified he would open his mouth to reveal funny pointed teeth. In a mixture of Arabic, English and French we explained what was wrong, what we needed to put it right and left it up to them to sort it out. We would find out what they did soon enough, but we had to go and meet Sven and David for a night on the town. The Dogsbane was put safely back in the Nissan. I slept in a fold-up bed, as it was the best the hotel could do.

The few days spent in Cairo passed in an alcoholic fog, including the horseback riding around the pyramids. Sven and I lost money at the casinos but the dark horse, David, won several thousand dollars at blackjack. As a group, the house lost on us and we drank a lot of their free booze.

The whole thing was a blast even though I slept in a rusty fold-up bed in one of the swankiest suites in Cairo. Serves me right for being so impatient with the hotel staff. At least we got our mail from around the world, including Chris's birthday cards from friends and family. We also got a call from Lisa, my friend Nick's girlfriend (now wife) to say that he would be in Heraklion on Crete on 5th and he'd be trying to get over the Russian wedding he had attended as best man.

We saw Sven and David off to the airport on the morning we were to leave for Alexandria. We'd had a lot of fun and I would be seeing them both at Christmas when I was planning to visit Abu Dhabi and Dubai. David had won enough at blackjack for them to have paid for their holiday and be returning with more money than they had come with. I call that a bargain, the best they'd ever had.

Alexandria was a breath of fresh air. There are few places in the Middle East one can get an invigorating breeze and this is one of them.

Alex was completely different to the rest of Egypt and I have since been back to make sure. The first look shows you that this truly is where East meets West. The mixture of architecture, people, and the breeze from the Mediterranean gave the city a very different feel but a closer look reveals the same cultural stupefaction. Someone had switched the city development, cleaning and redevelopment off about 100 years ago. Alexandria is at once like a little boy fresh from play in the garden and a somewhat sweet but dishevelled old man with a hint of urine.

Smelling of pee is probably not one of the things for which a city would want to stick in your mind but in some ways, it is indicative of Egypt, as it only seems to have its former glory days to recommend itself unto our gentler senses. It's no small accomplishment to have two of the ancient wonders of the world under your slightly whiffy, stained and crumpled raincoat though, eh?

Herodotus, an old-time travel writer of some repute, was 'the dude' for lists. He would have got on well with Chris. 'H' as he was to his mates, declared in the pub one night, as long ago as the 5th century BC, that there are seven Wonders of the, what would become the Ancient, World and all of them stimulated by genitalia. He listed them: "Listen up lads, there's the Great Pyramid, looks like a big pointy booby, right, and the lighthouse at Alex, very phallic with all those flames flying out the end, what else? Oh yeah, the Hanging Gardens, obviously inspired by pubic hair. Vaginas inspire all the temples, The Temple of Zeus, The Temple of Artemis at Ephesus and The Mausoleum at Halicarnassus in Bodrum, need I say more?"

"Weren't you exiled from Halicarnassus for trying to shag the ruler's wife, Artemisia?"

"That's a lie," says Herodotus. He continues unfazed, "last but not least, The Colossus at Rhodes - I rest my case."

"H, you need to get laid, mate, you've got sex on the brain."

"You may laugh, my latest book The Histories of Herodotus will be a best-seller for many years."

We tend to accept wonders with greater ease in these days of space travel, Internet and the Beckhams.

The lighthouse at Alex even appeared on Roman coins just as on currency today we portray famous monuments or people. Legend has it that the mirror at the top of the tower reflected the flames to produce more light to detect and burn enemy ships before they could reach the shore. Now there's something to interest the Beckhams innit – a large mirror?

If we wonder at the construction of the Burj Al Arab hotel in Dubai, the Eiffel Tower in Paris, London Bridge in Arizona, or any other great building it makes the lighthouse more of a wonder when the time is considered. If you take into consideration, the speed at which buildings have increased in size, the Alex lighthouse in today's terms would dwarf anything by a long way. The pyramids are . . . er . . . big but this is something else altogether.

The Lighthouse of Alexandria did not survive to the present day as it came down in two separate terrorist attacks by Mother Nature. The rubble fortified the city's walls.

Such a magnificent monument however makes its influence felt in the present day. From an architectural standpoint, the monument has been used as a model for many prototypes along the Mediterranean, as far away as Spain. And from a linguistic standpoint, it gave its name, Pharos, to many of the lighthouses in the world. Just look in the dictionary for the French, Italian, or Spanish word for lighthouse. That will probably be a change from looking up swearwords, eh?

You can also look in the French, Italian, or Spanish dictionaries for swearwords because these are the first words anyone wants to learn in another language anyway. And that is a wonder of the modern world.

If you look at a map of where the seven Wonders of the Ancient World were or are you might wonder, as I have on many occasions why they are all in such a relatively small area. I asked a rather groovy ancient historian such a question in my quest to unearth the weird, the wonderful or the cheap laugh. He said that that was where it was 'at' in those days.

So with Alexandria I had completed visiting all the sites of the Seven Wonders and hadn't realised it until that moment: The Great Cheops

Pyramid at Giza and the only that one is on the list and of course the only real remaining Wonder. The lighthouse at Alex or rather where it was supposed to have been is now an integral part of the city; The hanging gardens of Babylon, which I saw on a trip to Iraq (and I'll tell you about in a minute). That would be the one Wonder not that many people had seen or visited. The Temple of Zeus or the few bits and pieces of that I had seen on an earlier wandering as I did The Temple of Artemis at Ephesus and The Mausoleum at Halicarnassus in Bodrum – move along – nothing too much to see here.

From an earlier holiday in an earlier life The Colossus at Rhodes described by Pliny the Elder, as a marvel even lying on the ground - nothing much there at all these days of course. And, like so many of the wonders, an earthquake kneecapped the Colossus. Perhaps Mother Nature may have taken her toll because of the affront to her true wonders. For almost a millennium, the statue lay broken in ruins. In AD 654, the Arabs invaded Rhodes. They disassembled the remains of the broken Colossus and sold them to a Jew from Syria. The fragments made their way to Syria on the backs of 900 camels. That's what I love about ancient history. You can pull any old number out of a hat and no one is going to argue with you.

"Gawdon Bennet! Honest, guv, they came wiv nine hundred camels an' nicked da statue while we wuz asleep. OK?"

Let me briefly tell of a trip that led me to that Wonder of the Ancient World, The Hanging Gardens of Babylon in Iraq before Saddam discovered hiding in a hole in the ground, as a new pastime.

It was an exploratory trip for my employers at the time as we had been receiving queries from a number of people in Baghdad and Mosul but hadn't been able to reach them by phone, not surprisingly. I was keen to go and see Iraq for myself.

I flew there with Gulf Air but would have to return with Iraq Air. I wasn't looking forward to that but would deal with it as and when.

Surprisingly there were not too many questions asked of me at Saddam International but they did want to know how much hard currency I had and that I had to account for all of it when I left. Saddam's government was trying to maintain an artificially low exchange rate on the dollar of about four or five. On the black market, one could get three or four hundred to the dollar, because I did.

My taxi from the airport in Baghdad was uneventful and cost me tuppence ha'penny. I stayed at the Baghdad Sheraton because a missile had hit it during what my big sister, amusingly, called the Anarok War; she misheard me when I said Iran/Iraq War. It runs in the family I'm afraid. Anyway, I thought that should anything untoward kick off while I was in Baghdad I was in a place already hit by lightning. I took my rabbit's foot with me too; well, I would have had I had one.

Baghdad was a shambles with crowds of men standing around on street corners in shabby old army fatigues. Everyone was friendly but wary. Everyone wanted hard currency. There was no advertising but many hoardings. All of them carried pictures of the murdering sadistic scumbag otherwise known as Saddam Hussein. Theirs was poverty on a scale I hadn't seen in any other Arab or Middle Eastern country and I wasn't going to do any business, I found out on the first day. The enquiries were more about the hope for the future. It just meant waiting for another decade or two and more wars.

On the first night, I went into the bar of the hotel, which was akin to the scene in Star Wars at the spaceport when Obi Wan Kanobi goes looking for Han Solo. The band players didn't have multiple eyes though, in fact, there wasn't a band.

The shelves at the back of the bar carried every kind of alcohol one could think of, but all the bottles were empty. I nervously bellied up to the bar and asked for . . . a green bottle, about the size and shape of a milk bottle and a glass appeared in front of me. I want to believe the glass was smoked glass but I don't think it was. My green bottle had no lid or label and a song came to mind. The chap next to me had the same green bottle and the contents looked like beer.

Any port in a storm as my grandfather never said more than once or twice a day.

It smelled like beer, looked like beer and tasted like beer. It fact, it tasted bloody good. No other Westerners were in the bar and the Arabs in there didn't seem friendly. My reward for swapping pleasantries in Arabic with the bartender was a small plate of nuts. It was out and out favouritism as no one else had such luxuries. I was in.

Three green bottles standing on the bar; three green bottles far too empty by far, but if I have another green bottle I guess I'll probably fall. Then there'll be no green bottles standing on the bar.

At that mentally low point, I decided to turn in for the night, paid my bill, which was also tuppence ha'penny, got up, and fell towards the door. My legs refused to move initially and then I realised I had been drugged and that I was to be taken off to some hideous place to be tortured and made to give all my secrets away. As that would only take two or three minutes it was just as well I was drunk rather than drugged. I stumbled to the lift under the watchful gaze of my friendly barman. I slept well and didn't feel the anal probes of the alien abductors once.

Having chased down all the leads that I could, relating to business, I got around to reconfirming my flight. That is making sure they have a seat for me on the return journey, very important in the Middle East because if you don't do it they sell your seat. It was then that Iraq Air told me there was a delay of eleven hours, so I headed for Babylon happy to be wandering around rather than sitting in an airport with hordes of female shot putters who turned out to be the aircrew.

As I came out of the hotel the taxi drivers swarmed toward me, I didn't recognise any of them and called out, "Who speaks English?"

One of them said, "I do." We were married for the day at the extortionate cost of about US$20, which was good for him apparently and good for my expenses.

We paid to get in to the Hanging Garden after waking up the guard. The place looked like a building site where the bricks had the egomaniac of the day's name stamped on them. There was nothing really to see I'm sorry to say. Except perhaps a statue of a basalt lion that caught my eye. The statue was a lion screwing Nebuchadnezzar's daughter; apparently, she was up for almost anything. Now you don't know if I'm telling the truth do you? I am.

Back in Alex, we hit upon a small problem.

Ferries only go once a week to Crete from Alexandria and the one we were booked on wouldn't get in until the seventh, bugger! We called Lisa to get a message to Nick. He's the friend meeting us in Crete. That day August 1, so we had to drag a few days into the bushes and bludgeon them with a smelly kipper.

We spent the first night in the Alexandria Sheraton to assuage our addiction to five-star chain hotels, then went, and found a much cheaper deal to rest up before our 24-hour ferry trip. We spent a day on the beach a little way out of town and saw something we hadn't seen, either of us, for quite a while, miles and miles of golden sand with no one in sight in either direction.

It was a bit windy with sand getting into everything but the wind brought breakers onto the beach – something else we hadn't seen for quite a while, as the Arabian Gulf tends to be flat, flat or mostly flat. Too much body surfing ensued, too much because the next day we would ache, but that day we would be courageous body-surfers extraordinaire.

As I said, it had miles and miles of golden sands with no one in sight in either direction yet an Egyptian family with 42 children turned up and laid their towels out a few feet away from ours. The kids kicked sand over us, they were noisy, they stared and the family shared all of its food and drink with us. It's tough being British in Egypt. I believe Egyptians would even try to talk to people in elevators or on the tube. The family only stayed a while and they were our new best friends. In halting Arabic, we told them we were travelling to England by car. They laughed and give us 'that' look.

We had a very nice day until, not too far away, two young girls turned up. They were tall, blonde and pleasing to my lecherous eye. Their bikinis were . . . small I happened to notice as I cast a furtive glance in their direction. They made a playful run to the surf to get wet, definitely not to swim and then removed their bikini tops.

Whoa! This is the Middle East. Even in Egypt you didn't strip off, not in 1991 you didn't. This would be incarceration time, no matter who you were, if the police or some other official turned up. What a pickle.

Should we go over and point out their predicament, which meant we had been looking or do we ignore them, try to stay cool, and hope that no one else turn up and see what we can see. In any other country in the Middle East, I would have told them already like a stern father remonstrating with his daughter. We were torn.

We decided to forgo our self-deceiving coolness to save the girls from an awful fate.

I don't know how nudists do it but I found it very hard to look these girls in the eye, much as I wanted to – honest. We explained the situation to them or rather we tried to explain their potential predicament to them.

Typical, Chris and I get to meet the only two stunningly beautiful Scandinavians who speak no English. They were friendly and said things like, "England", "Mrs Thatcher" and "Football hooligans." It was not much of a conversation but our mime abilities only go so far. Not being that great at Pictionary I was seriously worried about acting out 'cover your boobs if you don't want to be locked up'. If Parker Games wants to use that in their next edition of the game, I'm fine with it. I find words like 'dense' hard enough to draw. The girls are being friendly laughing, being coy and jiggling about before us. Suddenly I'm thirsty as I look at the ground before me. Chris is smiling like a Labrador dog with its head out of the car window, but not for long.

The friendliness towards us ended when I handed them their bikini tops and waved my finger like an uncompromising school ma'am. The girls covered up and left and Chris wiped the drool from his lips, chin and chest.

He said, "That was tough, I had already crossed to the dark side, their beauty was intoxicating . . . It was the right thing to do – god damn it! I need a beer!"

I, on the other hand, felt old.

Had Chris and I been in Europe we would have just filled our eyes I guess, but being covered in the Middle East is important. It is a modesty issue which is supposed to apply to men and women as is my understanding of the Koranic verses I have read in English. Covering breasts and wearing outer garments to avoid harassment seems fair enough and certainly no more perverse than so many other things I could name to do with religion in general. I guess it's all down to interpretation.

While on the beach, and before the girls had changed our mindsets, Chris had been reading about the Mediterranean coast of Egypt and what there was to see. So we would hit the road again in the morning.

We had something important to do for Victor the chap in Abu Dhabi who helped us prepare the truck for its journey. He was an experienced overland driver. For everything he did, and it was a lot, including supplying us with spare parts, tuning, advice and much more, he wanted a postcard from Alexandria because he loved the film Ice Cold in Alex.

For those of you who don't know the film, it is a black and white British war film so it relies on acting rather than expensive special effects and pretty people. With twists and turns, John Mills, before his knighthood, plays a dipsomaniacal ambulance driver desperate to get to Alexandria to drink a cold beer, "so ruddy cold there's a sort of dew on the outside of the glass." Made me lick my lips just thinking about it. We definitely had an ice cold one or two in Alex for Victor.

We left the hustle and bustle of Alex and head to Mursa Mutrah towards the Libyan border. I got it into my head that I wanted to blow raspberries at Gaddafi. Chris helped me to see sense and I made do with vulgar signs in the general direction of Libya from the top of a pile of sand trying to be a dune outside Sidi Barani. We passed El Alamein along the way and decided to stop off on the way back to Alex.

In Mursa Mutrah, we found a very reasonable little hotel called the Hotel Blue Sky. The room was basic, clean and had three beds in case we wanted to invite someone to stay I imagine. It only cost 40 Egyptian pounds, which was about $10 for both of us and included breakfast of hard boiled egg, bread, marmalade and a small triangle of processed cheese – yummy!

The previous occupants or should I say tenants refused to leave when asked in English or Arabic so we removed them with a piece of paper once we had beaten their carapaces to a smooth runny consistency. They put up little real resistance.

Chapter Fourteen

The sun, sea and sand of Mursa Mutrah were soporific but emanated a real sense of checking time until we could move on. We had seen too many fantastic temples, too much stunning coral and even slept with beautiful suntanned girls. What more could a couple of hedonists want ?

"Will you shave my neck for me?" asked Chris

It was a jolting question, which I didn't question. Chris was obviously comfortable asking such a thing from me. This was about as intimate as it gets with another guy I guess. I shaved his neck and drifted back to where my mind wanted to go.

With time on my hands, I thought more about my father slowly dying and the Dogsbane now happily secreted away in the truck. I strengthened my resolve. I would still give it to him if that was what he wanted. How could I not?

I'd talked to Helen about my dilemma; we had become close in a short period. We were meeting up in London as soon as I got back. That's two people who would be able to have me jailed for murder. I wasn't doing very well at the not telling anyone thing. When I told Helen, her first reaction was, "You're kidding."

I assured her, "I am not."

"That's outrageous," she said. "How could your father ask you to do something like that, does he hate you or something?"

"No, I don't think he does and that is the hard thing, he's reaching out in some way," I said. "His timing's off but this is his way."

She frowned, leaned towards me and said, "You have to get rid of that stuff and tell him it's out of the question." I hadn't told her at that point it was lost anyway, but the conversation becomes more relevant now the Dogsbane is back in my care.

"I can't I've made a promise, well, I could, but I should do this for him, what if the tables were turned," I said.

"I'd expect him to say no to you," she said. Frowning at me, Helen changed her appearance in a heartbeat by smiling. She lightened the mood when she added, "You should get your father to convert to a religion where he doesn't think he's God."

Our conversation trailed away, no longer an argument in the making. Perhaps the only way to fight our demons is silently. It would be interesting to see if she had changed her mind by the time I got back to London. I wouldn't be long but there was some tavelling to do first.

Time passed soon enough. Our ferry would be leaving at 8:00 p.m. We would get there early; we had decided to arrive at about 3:00 p.m. because we wanted no possibilities of mistakes or cock-ups in administration.

We set off from Mursa Mutrah at 9:00 a.m., because on this day we were to pay our respects to the British cemetery in El Alamein.

I don't know about you but I have always had a bit of a fixation with cemeteries and graveyards. The temptation to do jokes about being dead centre or people dying to get there would be ignored on this occasion. I even felt a little apprehensive.

Looking at gravestones makes me wonder what sort of a person lies beneath. Would we have got on? Were they a good person? Were they scared or in pain when they died? Was death what they thought it would be?

This was the first time I had ever been to a military cemetery. A place that I had only ever heard talked about in awe and reverence. In a strange way today would be the closest I would ever really get to combat. Wars for my generation and beyond are more like Hollywood movies and Newsreels; we rely on CNN's Walter Rodgers and others to lay it all out for us. At 31, I was probably too old to get the military call even in the direst of situations for Britain, thank goodness, and now I am a father I know that I would do everything in my power to prevent my own children from having to fight.

The Mediterranean Coast Road was a pleasant drive without any of the usual surprises; we made El Alamein quickly and effortlessly. I imagine there were thousands of others in the 1940s who would have liked to say the same thing. The very road we had driven to get to El Alamein was the one where the fighting took place. Rommel versus Montgomery, Tommy against Hun, cut and thrust, tit for tat and casualty for casualty. Too many died.

The win at El Alamein, if the death of countless thousands on either side is a win, did much to restore Britain's badly battered self-confidence and prestige from France in 1940 and by the collapse in the Far East in 1941-2, which culminated in the loss of Singapore.

Sitting quietly and almost grandly on the road from Mursa Mutrah to Alexandria is a single-storey enclosure with a wide path and three-arched opening to the cemetery. It has quiet places to sit, panels on the walls with lists of names and the book, the black book with everyone's name in it, everyone that is who could be recognised or identified. There are graves shared by two or three soldiers in some places. They could not be separated as they were fused and so were buried together often, seemingly, unidentified.

Rows and rows of well laid-out graves lie among the occasional tree offering what little shade it could in the desert. The cemetery is immaculate, spick and span in the way only something military could be. I should have run my white-gloved hand over a gravestone to check for dust in a mock inspection.

Chris and I didn't say a word to each other for the time we were there. It was an incredibly moving experience, but it made me angry too.

Headstones engraved with simple words such as, we gave our only son for freedom, brought a lump to the throat and even a tear to the eye.

As a parent myself now, as I write this I'm crying, at the thought of giving my son or daughter up to war. If the very thought is unbearable, reality must have been living hell.

El Alamein is a remarkable place filled with remarkable people we must never forget. We should also make sure for our sons' and probably daughters' sakes that nothing like that ever happens again, and certainly not because some monkey-brained idiot in the White House surrounded by ghouls wants us to believe that there are Ws of mass destruction somewhere they would like to drill for oil. Not that I have strong opinions you understand and I apologise for the monkey comment, to monkeys.

We carried on to Alex for some lunch before joining the scrum for the ferry. How did we know it was going to be a scrum for the ferry? This was Egypt, that's how we knew.

I can bun-fight with the best of them I think, but there are times when it is smarter to ease back and let someone else do your dirty work. "The trick to a good scrum down is to have a good scrum half," I said to Chris. He didn't argue. "This is Omar and he will be our Mr Fix-it."

Omar was a ringer who cost us the princely sum of 25 Egyptian Pounds, about a fiver. He would take care of us, and the truck, all the way to the ferry. We were used to this system of letting someone else take the strain from living in the Middle East. The lack of hassle alone was worth a fiver.

Omar would run back to us asking for more money every few minutes. "Boss, numbers are wrong here," indicating paperwork.

"Boss, these dates are wrong," meaning we had overstayed our welcome. Oh, I bet American Express are crapping themselves right about now, I thought.

"Boss they need to search EVERYTHING!" meaning that if we paid more money, they would look the other way.

Total cost about 60 Egyptian Pounds and worth every piastre. We were sharing a little wealth.

Our paperwork, and this was the last time it would be an issue, was all over the place. The engine number on the paperwork was wrong; we had overstayed our welcome as we thought we would and they wanted to take everything out of the car and examine it in minute detail because we could see them doing it to the VW van full of German youths in front of us. Omar, our man of the moment, had the paperwork done; there was no searching of the truck and therefore no questions about Dogsbane. I was feeling protective towards it at that time. We were on the ferry in about thirty minutes. The Germans still had their smalls out on the road when we were on deck smoking cigarettes and patting ourselves on the back for being lazy, smart, or even, smart and lazy.

The stark difference between Egypt and getting on our Italian flagged ferry, the Something Something Express, which would take us to Crete, was remarkable. Once on board an Assistant Purser saw us to our cabin and made sure everything was tickety-boo, his words. The cabin was small but clean. It had a powerful shower, sink and a toilet, or head, we say now that we are aboard. There were two bunk beds with clean sheets.

Chris bagged the top bunk and curled up in a ball saying, "I think I've died and gone to heaven."

Our excitement at being on the ferry was tangible.

"Chris, am I mad, I feel as if I've been let out of prison or something," I said.

"Of course you're mad, but I know exactly what you mean. It's crazy but I just could not wait to get out of Egypt, I'd really had enough," he said.

"We're not just leaving Egypt mate, we are leaving the entire Middle East," I added. "As of tomorrow we will be in Europe, where things work properly, where we won't have to bribe anyone and where we'll probably be able to get a full English breakfast and a proper cup of tea."

And so that we are clear on this, I am totally happy about that statement, sod the snobbery, I want something that looks feels and tastes familiar for a change.

"Amen to that brother, might I suggest we drink English beer for the whole of the first night," said Chris.

"You can take the boy out of Shrewsbury, but you can't take the Shrewsbury out of the boy. Incidentally Mr Chris, I like the way you think, Nick will have been on Crete for nearly two days and will know where everything is in the way of partying I'm sure."

Even now, I am surprised at our strength of feeling atleaving the Middle East. We really had had enough of Egypt however, so it was time to move on.

We ate, drank and slept our way to Crete. It took about 24 hours and apart from a couple of games of Scrabble, we did nothing.

Arriving in Heraklion, Crete at around 6:00 p.m. local time Chris and I were on deck to watch and who should be standing on the quay, a head and shoulders above almost everybody else there but Nicky-boy?

"Heraklion or more properly 'Iraklion' was founded by the Saracens in the ninth century," said Chris in a very matter of fact way. "It later became the slave trading centre of the Mediterranean."

"I'm getting used to your telling me this stuff but it is a bit like banging your head against the wall."

"What do you mean?" asked Chris.

"It's nice when it stops for a while . . . Let's go and see what Nicky-boy has scoped out since he's been here."

"Crete's most famous for its Minoan culture," said Chris with a grin.

I had a bit of a scare at the Greek customs. The paperwork was fine because we didn't need any. We were British and therefore allowed to do anything legal we like. While we were dealing with our passports, another chap was looking in the back of the truck. We didn't pay him any attention.

"What's this?" said the port official loud enough for everyone nearby to hear and look.

Chris quite rightly got very interested in our passports while I headed for the Dogsbane hiding place. I felt remarkably calm. Here we were then, the answer to my dilemma all over again. 'I tried, Dad, they took the stuff off me in Crete, I couldn't find any more anywhere in Europe'.

"I can explain," I said as I approached the official.

"Well, you can't bring that in here," he said.

Feeling almost giddy as my head started to fill with the familiar buzzing sound, I rounded the back of the truck to find the offending item was not a jar filled with plant sap but my scuba air tank.

"Wha . . ."

"There is strict control on scuba diving on the island and you can only use air tanks from registered dive operators," he said.

"Why is that?" I said trying to gather my composure.

"Too many people taking valuable artefacts out of the country," he offered.

"OK, what do we need to do?" said Chris coming to my rescue.

"We'll seal it for you and you will be fined heavily if that seal is broken before you leave Crete."

It wasn't a problem; we did not intend to dive on Crete.

We get into the truck and Nick directed us to a reasonable pension he has found, at a price that is right, in a tourist town called Hersonissou. I can only describe this town as wild. It was full of beautiful women partying their minds out. The beaches were smothered in Scandinavian bathing beauties, there were some guys around too of course but this was not what was drawing our eyes. Living in the Middle East will do that to you.

Chris enjoying the view as much as I was, had a fact for the occasion, "Back in 2500 BC, warrior Minoan women began wearing a bra-like garment, shoving their bare breasts upward, it exposed their naked breasts from their clothing."

"Lisa wears stuff like that from time to time," said Nick.

"For fighting?" I said.

"Not fighting exactly. I like the dressing-up thing, probably because my dad used to have a lingerie factory I guess," replied Nick.

Nick had had a boring couple of days scoping bars making friends with bar owners, being invited to parties and generally having fun all over the place. I envied his easygoing nature that makes people warm to him. I have other friends like this, Tim and Steve. People want to be friends with them. I could say exactly the same thing as any of them to the same person but, I'd be in a fight, and they would have made a new friend. I don't understand it. They are good friends nevertheless. Nick has just travelled from Russia where he had been being someone's best man.

"You have to carry a crown around over his head for hours at these Russian orthodox weddings, I thought my arms were going to fall off," laughed Nick. "Man those guys can drink though; I believed my liver was going to give out."

"Did Lisa get hold of you then?" I asked.

"Yes she did but my flight from Moscow was already booked," said Nick.

"So, are you going to marry this girl, Nick?" I asked.

"I might, but once bitten, twice shy, she's great, really, but . . ." The look in his gave away what he was really thinking. He had already made his mind up. It was in the way he talked about her, he was stone in love.

"I envy you," I said, "sometimes I think I'd like to settle and sometimes I think I like having lots of different girlfriends."

"Well, you had to leave Abu Dhabi because you tried to drink the town dry! That doesn't sound like someone looking to settle down. What do you think, Chris?" joked Nick.

Chris and Nick had only met once before we set off but they were already getting on well, and ganging up against me. The three of us went out on a wild night, two nights in a row. We had to leave this place or face the financial and physical consequences. We decided to go and explore Crete. I also wanted to get Nick on his own to talk to him about my dilemma as he had special knowledge on these matters.

Nick's mother had died a few years earlier because of myalgic encephalomyelitis (ME) and she'd been in a lot of pain. Nick's dad, Deric Longden, had written a bestselling novel about the experience. The book titled Diana's Story was truly a wonderful book and an inspiration. It was a bestseller in its own right but by a quirk of fate every time Princess Diana did something newsworthy Deric sold more books. He was even accosted at a book signing because someone thought he was James Hewitt, one of Princess Diana's lovers. However, there were some things not written in the book that Nick had alluded to before and I wanted to get the full story from him and hopefully some insight into my own dilemma.

We drove North-ish. It was so different from Egypt. We filled Nick in on our adventure so far. We were just telling him about bare-breasted girls in Mursa Mutrah when it started to rain, only a shower.

Without speaking, Chris pulled the truck over to the side of the road; we all got out and turned our faces and outstretched palms up. It was a glorious feeling.

"I promise never to complain about rain again," said Chris.

"Oh man! How long has it been since you stood in a rain shower? said Nick.

"It's two years for me, longer for you I suspect," I said. "Doesn't it feel great?"

People were driving by and slowing down to look at the three weirdoes that now had their tongues hanging out and who may, or may not, have been doing a little jig. So uncool.

Getting back in the car, we realised how sad we must have looked but didn't really care. We continued north and tried to find somewhere to stay in a town called Chania. We found nothing in the price range we were prepared to pay. We decided to get out of town and travelled back a little way down the coast when in a most un-male way we ask a couple on the side of the road if they knew of any apartments for rent. Blow me down if they weren't just moving out of a place, and if we followed them up the hill they would introduce us to a really cool Greek couple who owned two buildings, one they lived in, the other in which they rented out rooms, at a reasonable price.

"Swipe me naked," said Nick. "That was more than a little lucky."

"Get used to it," I said. "We've been having luck like that since we left Abu Dhabi."

"And how," added Chris.

The introduction to the owner's wife who spoke no English, French, German, in fact, she only spoke Greek, was interesting. A Greek mum who would take no nonsense from a trio of naughty boys I imagined. She showed us the room soon to be empty. It was clean and even more importantly only 3,000 drachma, which at the time was about ten quid for the night for the three of us.

"Perfect, we'll take it," we said.

It had a roof garden covered with sun beds, flower pots and overlooked by the owner's balcony. We used it a lot in the first couple of days, which seemed to be another of those catching up times, we ate, slept, talked and drank beer. We were not interested in going anywhere.

We had been lying out there late one morning and the owner and his wife seemed to be having a disagreement about something. It involved knife waving and Chris was sure he heard the word goat mentioned. Perhaps the old boy was supposed to explain to the goat that it was the guest of honour at that night's dinner. It was time for us to have lunch and Chris went off to the shops, while Nick had decided on a shower prior to eating. Mr Chopoudopoulous, I didn't know what their real names were, eased up to his balcony closest to where I was lying baking and reading about why, according to an eminent quantum mechanic, that God did not play dice when Mr C, who had a voice like Herve Villachaize as Tattoo in Fantasy Island, said, "Eh, English! You kill my goat?"

It sounded at first like an accusation.

"What?" I squeaked. Coughing to clear my throat, "What did you say?"

"My wife wants me to kill the goat," he said sounding crestfallen. "You could kill a goat right?"

My manhood was being questioned, "I guess I could, but, but, wait a minute I can't kill your goat."

"Why not?" he asked.

"For one thing I'm a vegetarian," I offered. It was mostly true, I fell off the vegetarian wagon from time to time it was true. "Can't you kill the goat; surely you've done it many times."

"I have looked after this one from a baby, she is my friend, but if I don't do it my wife will do it . . and . . . and . . ."

"I'm sorry I can't help," I said. It was true; I had started thinking if I could kill a goat for a while before the thought dawned that it was preposterous. I'm a town boy, had it been the goat or me yes, I could have done it, but one does not see aggressive knife-wielding goats that often, even in Crete.

I told the guys over lunch, they laughed and said it could only happen to me. I think I'll do the shopping next time.

Nick's time was almost up and we still hadn't had the chance for a chat when Chris turned down the opportunity to come with us to the beach in favour of the roof. We told him to watch out for men bearing offers of goat's head stew.

On the beach it was hard to focus with all the bare-breasted nubile young women leaping about playing volleyball or Frisbee in front of us, you get the picture. I brought Nick up to speed over a beer at a little beach café. We had had to get off the sand for our sanity plus this conversation was not for anyone else's ears.

Nick said he was sorry to hear about my dad's cancer but as the rest of the story unfolded, he became increasingly quiet.

"My mum suffered a lot of pain and fought it, she fought it for a long time," said Nick. "It was wearing her down. I am not fully sure whether she died or maybe even took her life or maybe she didn't fight as much as she could have at the very end."

"Jesus, Nick, that must have been awful for you and your family," I sympathised.

"Let me tell you this though, if she had asked me what your father is asking you I would have done it in a heartbeat," he said, choking up. "I loved her very much but it was killing me to see her suffer so much, it was killing all of us, my dad most of all, but I wouldn't have hesitated had she asked."

"I guessed as much," I said.

"This may not be what you want to hear but you can't let your dad down in his hour of need."

We ordered more beer and took them back to the beach so the bouncing boobs could lighten our mindset.

Nick left the following day, back to Lisa and Dubai. They married not long after that. After dropping him off at the airport, Chris and I got back into the groove of doing nothing. It was as if we were recuperating from a long illness. We couldn't get up the energy to do anything other than eat, drink and sleep. I guess we were regrouping for Europe.

We took everything out of the Nissan and cleaned it. We repacked everything we weren't using, we checked over all the fluids, including the truck's. I took out the Dogsbane and regarded it as Hamlet did to Yorick's skull, then wrapped it up and put it back in its hiding place, there were no flashes of merriment for me either.

I did realise how spoiled we were. We hadn't roughed it at all in reality. How many travellers have a choice in teas? English Breakfast, Lemon-Scented, Earl Grey, Lime Blossom, Lemon and Lime, Lime Blossom-Mint or Camomile. Tough life.

Having been on the road now for 50 days we took stock of our situation. We'd slowed our spending and with it our activity. If there was a connection, we couldn't see it. Still lazing around too much we decided that it was time to move on. We went to Chania to book a ferry to mainland Greece.

On the way to Chania, I realised it had been some time since Chris had assailed me with any facts.

"Have you given up on the facts and figures then, Chris?"

"No, I've just felt so lethargic, I can hardly move it seems," he said, sounding as if he meant it.

And this is where it starts. The magnetic pull to England.

"I've been thinking about getting back to England," said Chris.

"That's bizarre – me too," I offered. "But why, there's nothing for us there really."

"I know, weird isn't it, we must have the fifty-day itch," said Chris.

Over the next few days, we got into a rut of sleeping until lunchtime, then getting up and having breakfast. Chris would sunbathe on the roof and I would go to the beach. We were having personal time, I guess. We were doing nothing and it started to get on my nerves.

One day on the beach, I was observing the hell parents put their children through so they will damn well have memories to look back on. The kids were obviously in distress but the parent with the camera was relentless.

"Robin, Robin, put this decaying seaweed on your head and hold this dead seal that was caught in the fisherman's nets and killed for its trouble. Don't make that funny face; it will make a good photograph. Don't vomit, that will spoil the picture . . . oh you just think of yourself you, you selfish little brat."

And so it goes. These kids will grow up, get married, have children of their own and then torture them in the same way. Who says genetic engineering is a bad idea?

The following day I set off for the beach and whilst parking the Nissan I notice a car full of girls stuck in soft sand at the edge of the beach. I offer help and wish Chris were here for his German language skills. After towing their car out of the sand and parking it somewhere a little firmer, they asked me if I would like to join them on the beach. Well, three stunningly beautiful girls with fit young tanned bodies and long blonde hair - nah - I think I'll give that a miss. The recurring theme of tanned and blonde doesn't elude me. I thought it odd because if I had a type of girl I found attractive it wasn't usually tanned and blonde. One of life's little mysteries.

"Sure, that would be thun," I said, as my tongue was stuck between my teeth. "My name is Greg," I should have added to that, and I am a sad git but I had to pinch myself to make sure I wasn't dreaming. I am so pleased I played the Good Samaritan.

"This is Madison unt Mallory unt I am Morgan, vee are taking vacation from da college, ja."

We walked toward the beach and I was on the end of some admiring glances from guys heading in the other direction, but not because they liked the look of me. "Really," I said, "what are you guys studying?"

"It is difficult in English, we work in da hospital wiz da bones and muskals, ja?" said Morgan.

"Really," I said, having a serious problem with the ever-widening grin on my face. I was heading to the beach with three beautiful physiotherapy students and Chris was on the roof, on his own. I would take pictures for him.

The girls danced around topless for me and put suntan lotion on one another and on my back for me. I spent a lot of time on my front actually. They were good fun, we agreed to meet up, and they would come with Chris and me to Chania to book our ferry for the mainland and have dinner and so on. They were leaving Crete tomorrow afternoon.

We got our ferry booked and wandered from bar to bar in Chania having a great time. I shouldn't have driven, but I did because the girls were coming back for drinks and, they had already been so friendly. I don't think I had laughed, danced and snogged quite as much before or ever would again. The girls were intent on enjoying their last night and for some reason Chris and I were the ones who were the focus of those intentions. We were sorry to see them go whenever it was they went. We were completely whacked and went back to sleep to try to carry on the dream.

Our ferry left in two days.

Physically booking the tickets had been interesting. We were told ferries to Greece left every night at 8:00 p.m. We told the booking agent who had no personality and all the expressiveness of a recent botox recipient we have a car.

"Very good, sir, shall I book you on tomorrow's ferry then?"

No arguments, no masses of paperwork, no rushing to Turkey to buy a ticket that meant we had to leave in four years and go via Rio de Janeiro.

The night following the night out with the German physiotherapists Chris and I went back to Chania, because we thought it was a cool place. It was then that we got into our only real fight with each other.

I can be like a dog with a bone at times. I don't realise I'm doing it but on reflection it must be why I have had some measure of success as a journalist. I ask personal questions and keep asking them until I get the answer I'm looking for; it's not always a pleasant experience.

Chapter Fifteen

"Tell me about your childhood?" I asked Chris only half-joking. We are in Chania in a bar, for a change, sitting outside and enjoying a gentle Cretan evening breeze, what little of it there was.

"We're in a bar, there's no couch and you're not a trick cyclist," said Chris.

"You're right, but I've lifted my skirts for you. I thought you might like to reciprocate. You mentioned some abuse earlier, anything you want to add?" Larry King might not approve of my technique, but what is the point of fannying around?

"It's personal, it's my business and I choose not to discuss it," said Chris getting a little more morose than I thought.

"Come on, Mr Uptight, unwind and talk about something instead of spouting facts that no one can refute," I said pushing a little too hard.

He slammed his beer down hard enough to break the glass, pushed past me, and walked off. I sat and allowed the bar staff to fuss around a bit and clear up before I paid the bill and left with my cool in tatters.

I walked along the quay and knew I would find him soon. He wasn't going to walk back to Britain or the apartment for that matter. I know that because I wouldn't and we were, for all of our differences, quite alike. I would apologise for being without sense and sensibility. He would confess to not liking Jane Austen books and admit to what was bugging him; well, that's the way I imagined it would work out.

I caught up with him sitting by the water's edge.

"Don't start," he said.

"I have no intention of starting," I said. It was a lie but he wasn't to know that.

"I don't have very happy memories of my childhood. You think it's normal at the time, but it isn't. Verbal abuse does just as much damage as physical," he said.

For the first time in my life, I knew what writers meant about someone looking like a wounded animal. It's in the eyes. That was a can of worms where maybe the lid should stay on. I had a feeling this would not be the last time I would think that.

"Hey, don't sweat it, mate," I said. "Talk if you want, or tell me to mind my own beeswax . . . I won't, but you can tell me anyway."

He laughed, offered his hand and I helped him up so that we could go and drink some more and flaunt the drink driving rules of which I don't think there were any at that time. I'll tell you why I think that too.

As Chris and I headed back to the Nissan with a few beers under our belts, we noticed a local coming out of a bar and going into the side alley to retrieve his motor scooter. Before he got on and tried to ride it, he obviously needed a pee. Now I have every sympathy with this guy because I've been this drunk but it is funny to be watching rather than participating.

Confusing the order in which things have to go, this guy relieved himself over the saddle of his scooter before sitting in it. Something registered in his brain but I couldn't be certain what that was. It looked like something was missing. Then the most remarkable thing, remembering that this guy could hardly walk, let alone drive; he started the engine and rode off in a perfectly straight line. He'd probably been doing it for years.

Tomorrow would be our last day on Crete and we had done nothing culturally, so we decided to 'do' Crete in one day. The funniest part of that statement is that we didn't even give it a second thought.

Doesn't everyone 'do' Crete in a day?

When the apostle Paul was on his way to see Caesar he stopped on Crete. I believe he may have been looking for a beer, Acts, Chapter 27, according to my research. Actually, Paul was a prisoner of the Romans under a centurion called Julius of the Augustus Band, whom you will remember had a hit with Agadoo.

Crete in the old days tried hard at being the Switzerland of the Aegean. They made one mistake and learned from it. Doesn't sound like much of a title, does it? But, the old days I'm talking of were before Domino's Pizza. In those days, around Crete was just about the most important place in the world. Look at the map of the Seven Ancient wonders of the World to get an idea.

Crete chose not to get involved during the Persian Wars after consulting the Delphic Oracle, the snappier name for the Pythia at Mount Parnassus. The Cretans, not to be confused with cretins, were reminded what had happened to them after they sent ships, on the side of Menelaus, in the Trojan War. Brad Pitt (in his crap movie Troy) swam across the sea, jumped up in the air and hundreds of them fell dead because he wasn't wearing anything under that tight-fitting leather outfit.

Pythia: You lot again, don't you ever learn?

Cretan delegation: Oh, 'ello, we were just passing and wondered if you could give us a hand with a dilemma what we was discussing, like. (Cretans often lapse into a form of Cockney at the end of a sentence of dialogue; at least they do not speak in rhyming couplets).

Pythia: Don't get involved or you'll get your collective arses kicked.

Cretan delegation: Right, OK, thanks for that . . . how's the family?

Pythia: Look, just bugger off will you I have a right dose of the vapours today.

So, Crete again chose neutrality during the Peloponnesian War and remained very much on the periphery during Classical and Hellenistic times with Cretans gaining a reputation as liars and pirates, which is better than getting your arse kicked. A hard 'rep' is not such a bad thing when you're an island in the middle of all the Classical, Hellenic and Byzantine period action.

After seventy years of trying to find Crete, because they were into marching more than sailing at that time, Romans finally got their hands on Crete in 67 BC after some very bloody struggles. The Cretans were a bit miffed at the 'pirates and liars' tag by then, which had hung around for so long, and thought, they might try to kick some butt themselves.

They got kicked up in the air, as they saying goes, and the Romans then proceeded to misrule and almost, at times, completely ignore the island. Well, once you've invaded an island and done all your raping and pillaging, what else is there to do?

Although Chris and I had attempted some raping and pillaging, which I think involved a goat and lots of alcohol, it was only half-hearted so we had to make up our minds quickly about what we were going to see in our one day left. The obvious choice would be Knossos, if only for the name, but Chris, not surprisingly, had done his homework. Knossos is a bit of a dead loss unfortunately, if you like your history unadulterated, and the far better site is Phaistos. The latter was more 'original' and less staged.

Crete is a good place to holiday because it has just about everything anyone might need. If you haven't been, I recommend it highly. I have never been so relaxed without the aid of strong drugs.

We managed to get around a few things after starting with Phaistos but one thing is worthy of mention. Don't go to Egypt and see all the best they have to offer of ancient times and then visit a pile of bricks, with a less than magnificent staircase and a couple of old vases. It rather spoils it. We were spoilt; I mean, short of a Sistine Chapel, what was going to impress us?

We went back to our little Cretan apartment tired and a little crest-fallen. Could history or architecture ever impress us again?

Repacking the truck, I got a little knot in my stomach from seeing my jar but I dismissed the thoughts that rushed to mind. It wasn't easy as there's not much else in there. We had most of our other stuff washed, pressed and generally tarted up and it was almost like setting off all over again. The European mainland was next, we'd come a long way already.

We said good-bye to our landlady and her husband. She was sad to see us go, he was happy because we left our half-empty alcohol bottles with him. They offered us some goat stew for our flask but unfortunately, we'd lost our flask. That's our story and we're sticking to it. But, I had to ask.

"Mr C, who killed the goat?" I asked.

"Don't ask, English, I have lost a little friend to my belly."

I had the feeling he went through that pain every time an animal was fattened. I also had the feeling that he never killed the animals but that his wife never fully let him off the hook.

The ferry port at Heraklion was efficient and organised so can't possibly have anything to do with Greece or Egypt. The ferry was on time and took us to where we wanted to go, reinforcing my statement about Greece.

A year earlier, I had taken a holiday in Greece and wanted to roam the islands a little before I went to a two-week residential course on the island of Skyros. I was going to clean up my act and was intent on a fortnight of Tai Chi, Yoga, a macrobiotic diet and some windsurfing. I had also heard that men were outnumbered two to one, which were my kind of odds.

I left for Skyros after attending an extremely wild party in Mykonos known as the gay island, and let's face it, gay people know how to party. They also, apparently know how to put quite strong hallucinogenic drugs into one's drink.

I do not condone spiking drinks in any way as it is irresponsible and dangerous but as I had travelled that road many years before it was more of a pleasant surprise and a bonus for me. I worked at a psychiatric hospital in Cambridge while I was studying so I know drugs are not always that way for everyone.

After booking a ferry from Mykonos to Skyros and having the ticket in my pocket I let the drug do what it wanted in my head whilst maintaining a semblance of control. I had to be on the quay at 7:00 a.m.

I was there, still hallucinating, as the ferry arrived, and I got on. I was a little sluggish but compos mentis enough to ask if it was the ferry for Skyros. It was and being slightly paranoid about my state I asked a couple of other members of staff on my way to the deck where I intended to get some sleep. Everyone, including the blue lizard eating deck furniture, agreed that this was the ferry for Skyros. I fell into a wonderful dream-filled sleep.

When I awoke by my reckoning, we were about twenty minutes from Skyros. I grabbed my bags, ignoring the stares from people who had been sitting near me, listening to my sleep-filled ranting, and prepared to disembark.

The blue lizard had morphed into an officious member of the crew and looked none the worse for wear from eating all that furniture. Don't ask me how I knew she was the blue lizard you'll just have to trust me.

"Today we will not stop at Skyros," the crewmember, formerly a blue lizard, said.

"But I have a ticket that says I am going to Skyros on this ship, you told me earlier we were going to Skyros," I said. My argument could get a bit shaky if they denied telling me that or anything else for that matter. Come to think of it, they could have denied we were on a ship.

"Yes, but we had to change - there is a strike in the port we now are bound for Skiathos," she said matter-of-factly.

"I don't want to go to Skiathos today. I am meeting transport in Skyros to start a course tomorrow," my voice was rising in volume and attracting other, larger, male members of staff.

"I'm sorry there is nothing I can do. You will have to arrange transportation from Skiathos, there are many ferries, planes . . ." Her voice trailed off, for a very good reason, she was walking away from me. My audience and experience of Greek ferries was at an end.

In Skiathos they had no ferries. Not for want of trying, I couldn't get to Skyros that day. I had to take a hydrofoil to Athens, where I stayed overnight in the Athens Meridien, nice chillers on the showers by the way, the hotel booked me a flight to Skyros and I arrived a day late and several hundred pounds lighter in the wallet. I am just so New Age in the way I travel. I probably could have got there for sixpence on a pedalo. However it was a great two weeks.

Getting off the ferry from Crete (this time) that had left on time, arrived on time and was plain sailing seemed too easy but that's what it was and fairly priced too. There was no searching getting on the ferry or getting off it. They didn't even look in the car, they saw our British passports through the window and that was enough. The Dogsbane was in Europe. It was now all up to Dover and the British Customs to save me from further dilemma. Damn, I was not feeling confident of getting into trouble with this stuff and having to give it up.

Chris and I were in Piraeus, Athens. We were on mainland Europe and there should be no more arguing about paperwork with border patrols. We might have got some funny looks with Arabic number plates.

Chris and I were 'templed' out but in Athens, one has to see the 'Sacred Rock' or Acropolis hill. Said hill is not one pile of rocks but four. Pile of rocks is a little unfair for buildings that look good considering their construction was in or around that wonderful Hellenic period.

The Parthenon is the most famous of these structures, whose dedication was to Athena Parthenos, the patron goddess of Athens and built of Pentelic marble. Pentellic marble is fine-grained, pure white and quarried from the Pentelli mountains north of Athens.

"The Elgin Marbles are also made of this marble," according to Chris.

There are few people in the world who would not recognise the Parthenon's silhouette.

"The Erechtheion is a lesser-known structure on the hill built around the same time as the Parthenon. And, the Propylaea is the monumental gateway of the Acropolis, designed by the architect Mnesikles and built in 437-432 BC," said Chris getting into his stride.

The Temple of Athena Nike, now there is a name that everyone in the world knows. Well, everyone in the Third World because they have to work in Nike sweatshops, breathing harmful fumes for one American dollar per day so that fashionistas of the training shoe, or sneakers, as my wife calls them, can pay hundreds of pounds for a pair of plimsolls that have been attacked by a waffle iron. Nikae means victories, so I have to assume that means victory of money over sense. A multi-billion pound industry is still growing thanks to a puff of smoke reflected in a mirror. That puff of smoke is toxic to small children chained to work-tables. Nike is making an effort to change so hurrahs, but it is the tip of an iceberg that includes globalisaed abuse of third world countries.

We cashed some traveller's cheques in Athens and moved on. While we were getting out cash, we noticed a picture of Mr Gorbachev on the front of a newspaper and tracked down an English version. We could only find a copy of The Sun so it had no news in it, but old Gorby apparently has a nice rack. Just kidding I saw something about an arrest.

They didn't lock Gorbachev up; I believe it was more of a house arrest. Not much has changed since then really apart from space tourism. Nevertheless, this is one of the seminal points in our global history.

We didn't bother with that story too much after that. We didn't realise it was the fall of the Soviet Union; we want to go and sniff hallucinogenic gases at Delphi. Our priorities were ours.

The Oracle of Delphi in Greece was the telephone psychic of ancient times. People came from all over Europe to call on the Pythia at Mount Parnassus to have their questions about the future answered, as much as the Cretans did. Her answers could determine when farmers planted their fields, when an empire declared war or whether blue lizards should eat deck furniture on ferries.

The Pythia, a role filled by different women from about 1400 B.C. to A.D. 381, was the medium through which the god Apollo spoke.

According to legend, Plutarch, a priest at the Temple of Apollo, attributed Pythia's prophetic powers to vapours. Other accounts suggested the vapours might have come from a chasm in the ground. This traditional explanation, however, failed to satisfy scientists. In 1927, French geologists surveyed the oracle's shrine and found no evidence of a chasm or rising gases no matter how many tins of beans they ate. They dismissed the traditional explanation as a myth.

In the August 2001 issue of Geology, it reveals that two faults intersect directly below the Delphic temple. The study also found evidence of hallucinogenic gases rising from a nearby spring and preserved within the temple rock. Chris and I believed the story all along and have no confidence in the French geologists anyway.

Lying on the grass at Delphi trying to have a free hallucinogenic experience, I shared my concerns with Chris, "It seems like this isn't going to cut it. It's all down to Dover now and I don't hold out much hope there. I'm going to have to give him the Dogsbane aren't I?"

"It looks that way," he agreed.

"Bugger it."

Chris drove for the rest of the day and we didn't say much. I was thinking about getting back to England, about going through Customs at Dover and, funnily enough, I was thinking about my father. I was alternately feeling sorry for myself and then him. It was a bit like a mental version of pulling the petals of a flower. I feel sorry for him, I feel sorry for me, I feel sorry for him . . . before I ran out of petals I fell asleep.

Waking up as we reached Igoumenitsa, Chris said, "Welcome back, you were away with the fairies for quite a while. I've stopped filled up, stopped and had coffee. If there were any aliens about you'd probably have a sore arse too."

"Must have been the vapours at Delphi, I guess," I said.

"Maybe . . . er . . . who is Maurice?" asked Chris, "And John?"

"I don't . . . they're my grandfathers' names," I realised.

"Well you were having a good chinwag with them, I can tell you," he said.

"I have to tell you I feel refreshed," I said. "You know I shouldn't worry about my father, he has to do things his way and I have to do mine my way."

Chris smiled. "And what does that mean exactly?"

"I'm not sure yet, but I think I will be. I think I'm feeling more relaxed about this whole thing the closer I get to England," I said.

"I hope so for your sake."

We were close enough to Albania to attack if we wanted and seeing how most Albanians had moved to California we might well have taken them. We had other things on our minds however, such as how disgusting Iguanapoopamitsa was. We found a hotel not fit for cockroaches so there weren't any there; they were staying in the fancy place up the road. It had a star.

We tried to find some decent food in Iguanapoopamitsa and there wasn't any so we ate what there was, which I think was road kill or pigswill or something. It wasn't good - did I convey that?

Tum-ti-tum a.m. and we were in a five-mile queue for the ferry which wasn't there, the ferry, not the queue. Chris and I were early as was our wont, but the Italians going home and the Greeks leaving Greece were all there before us. As ever, there were inordinate numbers of German holidaymakers too. Did they know something we didn't?

When the ferry arrived, another problem confronted us. Another problem apart from that the boat or ship, whatever you want to call it, was a heap. If I weren't already grumpy and itching to get out of Greece I would have seriously considered waiting for another ferry. The ferry, let's call it the SS Shitheap, made the one from Aqaba to Nuweiba in Egypt look like the QE2.

The problem this titanic bathtub faced was as yet unknown to us. However, when one sees a diver jumping from the side of one's ferry with a huge monkey-wrench in his hand, what should one do? One craps onerself that's what one does.

The monkey-wrench fixed whatever it was after some time. No explanation was forthcoming and no one asked. Perhaps they were used to such developments. The 9:00 a.m. ferry left at 11:20 a.m. We were uneasy but resolute about our commitment to get to Italy sooner rather than later. On board the hits kept coming when Chris bought two teas, placing them on the table I sipped my first and almost covered Chris with the contents of my mouth. Tea made with seawater is not pleasant and I think inadvertently we had uncovered part of the problem with our rust bucket. It was letting in water to places it shouldn't. We felt so much better knowing that. We survived the day on our reserves of Mars bars and crisps.

The ferry chugged its way across the straights of Otranto to Otranto, which was the mirror image of Iguanapoopamitsa only in Italian. Otranto is easier to say than lizardypoopycacky. It sits on the stiletto heel of Italy's boot, right about where you would put a blakey, you know, one of those metal things that are supposed to protect your shoes from wear. We left Otranto immediately, because it was too much like Iguanapoopamitsa and drove north for a while, because we were on a mission. Chris had read about a town called Lecce that is off the well-beaten tourist track and has an architectural style all its own. For two jaded travellers this could be the fillip needed to get us out of ourselves.

First things first, beer and pizza, we were in Italy for goodness sake. The beer was good and the pizza outstanding. We had time for a little wander around the streets.

"Lecce is a city not a town," said Chris.

"I stand corrected, Herr Professor."

He continued, "The local sandstone, tinged a warm pink, is so easy to work with that it fostered the rise of a local style called 'Barocco Leccese' as ornate and intricate as any the world has seen."

"You read very well," I said with a tinge of sarcasm, as by now, we were both familiar with the game we played.

We took a stroll down the Via Palmieri, stopping to watch artisans working the local sandstone in their shops. We carried on down to Piazza Falconieri, overshadowed by the magnificent Palazzo Marrese. This was an impressive place and if it hadn't been for Chris, I never would have heard of it.

"Two caryatids flank the portal and the balcony rests on splendidly carved shelves," said Chris.

"Forgive my ignorance but what's a carry-attid?"

"Her and her," indicated Chris pointing at two draped stone maidens acting as columns. "They don't have to be women, but they usually are."

"You know stuff, you," I said.

We got to a shop at 21 Via Ribichi that sold knick-knacks and we probably would have gone in if we hadn't seen the wine shop next door. It sold a wonderful selection but we were up for trying the Salento wines. We bought a few bottles and walked past the quite lovely church of Gesù, not his only one I reckon, on our way back to the Nissan.

It was getting late and, for a change, we had no plan about what to do for sleeping. We drove on towards Naples along the coast road, staying off the big roads as much as possible.

Getting tired and with no hotels, campsites or pensions in sight we pulled off the road into a lay-by that had a little dirt road off it and we spent the night in the car after a bottle or two of wine. Tomorrow we would reach Naples with a minor sidestep into Pompeii, as one does.

Chapter Sixteen

"See Naples and die, was a definite possibility if you were sexually active in 1495," said Chris.

"OK, you have my attention," I said.

"There was a really bad syphilis epidemic in 1495, the epidemic spread outward from Naples to all of Europe. 'Naples' became a common euphemism for the Pox."

"A dose of the Naples, hmm, sounds yummy. I just thought the saying about dying came about because it was pretty and therefore you'd never need to see another city, so is that where that saying comes from?" I asked.

"I'm not sure because there is a place nearby to Naples on the map called Mori, which as you know from your years of enforced Latin means 'to die', but it could also be to do with Vesuvius erupting or maybe even the mafia," said Chris. "Incidentally, the Arabs used to call syphilis the Christian disease."

"Your capacity for facts and figures is staggering," I said.

"Yeah, stops me thinking about anything else probably." I let that slide. It wasn't the time for delving into the black hole of Chris's psyche.

Driving around the southern Italian coast was very beautiful and we would soon be in 'Syph-city', but first we were to look at the buried city. Pompeii would not be famous if it were not for Vesuvius.

*   *   *

In AD 79, Pompeii and Herculaneum, buried by a pyroclastic flow that the inhabitants watched approach, left the modern world an amazingly crisp snapshot of the first century. Pliny the Younger recorded the dreadful event in a letter to his friend Tacitus. His uncle, Pliny the Elder perished, leaving the family with at least one more choice for names, Pliny the Pockmarked, called 'dibs'.

Pompeii is the ancient architectural and anthropological version of the Mary Celeste. It looks like the inhabitants left recently, well, it would if you couldn't see their shadows cast on the wall where they vaporised. The story is far more exciting than seeing it, I think, but again this is probably because I have just spent five or six weeks in Egypt with piles of rocks that are over 10,000 years old and even better preserved than Pompeii in many places without the aid of pyroclast.

Coincidentally, August 24, the day of the catastrophic volcanic eruption that buried the city and obscured the sun on a mild and otherwise pleasant afternoon was also the date of the Vulcanalia, the festival of the Roman god of fire, according to Pliny the Spooky.

Covering something over with ash for sixteen centuries seems to keep it in good condition but I wouldn't recommend it for meringues.

Chris added, "Vesuvius has erupted about three dozen times since 79 AD, most recently between 1913-1944. That eruption may well be the end of a cycle that began in 1631, according to my notes."

"I imagine there are quite a few people who would want to agree with that statement," I said.

*   *   *

On to Naples, this to my mind, is a toilet-bowl of humanity, full of weirdoes and the flotsam and jetsam of life, which may not be a popular statement but my own snapshots tell me I speak the truth. Litter and garbage strewn in the streets coupled with high unemployment and rampant crime figures. But guess what, I loved it. This is a place in which you need to spend a lot of time to experience it truly. It has an earthiness and it feels real.

People watchers of the world should descend on Naples, but don't have anything valuable about your person as it will be stolen. When and if it changes I'll be very surprised. An old girlfriend of mine told me that it is also the bottom pinching capital of the world; fortunately, I missed that but it explained why she spent so much time there. She was not a typical woman.

Also, note to everyone, just as one should not mention the war to Germans, you probably shouldn't mention it to Italians. Worse than that, these days, is that you really shouldn't mention the Mafia either, especially in this region of Italy, it's a bit like an Arab today telling Customs at JFK airport that he's in America for flying lessons. This is not Hollywood or some cheesy cable network series. This is reality. They have real Mafiosi here and they are short on patience with stupid tourists thinking life is a TV show.

If reality is too real for you, do yourself a favour, go to Sorrento and look at everything through rose-tinted glasses from a pleasant distance, unless you like getting dirty.

Rather than hanging around and contracting something horrible, we decided to head up the coast toward Rome. Before we hit the big one, we took another brief sidestep to Monte Cassino as Chris's suggestion. He gave me the background.

The strategic position of Monte Cassino has made it the repeated scene of battles and sieges from antiquity. What better reason for a visit? In World War II, the Battle of Monte Cassino was, in fact, a costly series of battles fought by the Allies with the intention of breaking through the Gustav Line, seizing Rome and linking up with Allied forces contained within the Anzio 'pocket'. I seem to be more than usually fascinated by war these days, or is that a British thing?

The capture of Monte Cassino allowed the British and American divisions to begin the advance on Rome, which fell on June 4, 1944 only two days before the Normandy invasion. The cost in human life was in the tens of thousands from the forces of the USA, the UK, India, Canada, Australia, South Africa and New Zealand, a real coalition of the willing. One of the forces hardest hit were the Polish however, and they ended up taking the hill on the fourth attempt.

Having seen the before and after pictures it is terribly difficult to believe they are of the same place. The historic monastery of Monte Cassino wasn't merely demolished, every rock, every blade of grass, everything was entirely pulverized. Fortunately, the Germans had removed Monte Cassino's irreplaceable library for safekeeping to Rome at the start of the Battle. The other way to read this would be that they'd stolen it and hadn't shipped it to Berlin yet, but that would sound terribly cynical in the face of so much devastation and death.

Rebuilding the site, to my mind would have seemed futile; happily, I can tell you no one pays any attention to my mind. The historic buildings are utterly gone and in their place are some of the gaudiest and hideously over-the-top buildings one could ever have the misfortune to visit, particularly the church.

Chris surprised me. "I'm not going in there."

"What, why not?" I asked. "It was your idea to come here before going to Rome."

"That is a disgrace. People die, starve, there is child molestation especially in the Catholic Church and what do they do. They spend millions on a celebration of their own grotesqueness. I will not enter that building."

"You're not a raving Protestant or something, are you?" I asked.

"Like you, I don't believe in religion," he spat. "I thought this would be a nice place to visit. Instead, it is a gilt and Rococo monstrosity. A few cushions and some hookers and you got a glitzy brothel."

"Hang on; I think religion is good for a lot of people, and considering where we are I'm definitely going to hedge my bets, it's just not for me, and obviously not for you," I replied. "I won't be long but I've got to look."

Consecrated by Benedict XIII, the opulence of Monte Cassino is an assault to one's eyes. Benedict XIII, né Pietro Francesco Orsini, was Pope from 1724 to 1730 and three Benedicts prior to the current one. He succeeded Innocent XIII in 1724. At first, he called himself Benedict XIV, due to the superstition that the number thirteen brings bad luck, but afterwards altered the title and died almost immediately when a statue of the Virgin Mary fell over pushing the poor chap onto the halberd of one of the Swiss guards supposedly protecting him. Not really, but it would have made a great story, wouldn't it?

In richness of marbles, only the Certosa at Pavia, the Carthusian Monastery, surpasses the interior of Monte Cassino, and the first impression is certainly one of astonishing magnificence. On closer inspection, however, the style is decadent, especially in the plasterwork of the ceiling, while the enormous profusion of inlaid marble and gilding produces a slightly nauseating effect.

I had Chris's comments rattling around the internal space in my head, which had been set aside for a larger brain than the ganglion of nerves twisted together at the top of my spine looking decidedly like tourists who have lost their passports. I feel I have to restate that I prefer graveyards - they're more honest.

A question in my mind was why those looking for peace and contemplation in a monastery need all that decoration and gaudiness. To my undemanding wits, simplicity and a lack of visual stimulation would be more fruitful. I know nothing, and should probably keep it to myself.

Chris had worked himself up into a frenzy about this place and I was too much of a blunt instrument to get to the bottom of his can of worms. You could make out the wriggling but I wouldn't be able to get to the worms and probably just as well. I had the feeling, this was a job for a professional.

Putting the tent up was easy, Chris was an old hand because he'd done it in Sinai. It was deceptively large, somewhat like Dr Who's Tardis. Alright, that's a lie but you could sleep three as long as they were friends. On the outside, it did not look that big.

The campsite doubled as an orchard, among other things, and some of the apples were ripening early. I know this because I was sitting in the truck making notes when, in what was otherwise quiet solitude, an apple with a flair for Newtonian physics dropped onto the roof of the Nissan and I nearly had heart failure. Chris, I thought, was going to lay an egg. He laughed so hard and long I thought he might be losing the plot. He couldn't talk about it for days after without laughing. It was funny, in a slapstick kind of way, but not that funny.

On Saturdays it seems no one works in Italy, except the thieves, they never get a day off, which leads me to believe that crime is not as organised at they would like to make out. Anyway, we wanted to buy food and couldn't so we went back to the tent to eat emergency rations because we were going to go to Rome very soon. We read and caught up on journals with the intention of turning in for an early night. The local population had another idea in mind; the campsite doubled, or is that trebled, as a park at weekends so they decided on raucous family picnics surrounding our tent.

"Jesus," said Chris. "They'll probably be there until Monday now, how can we get any sleep with that racket going on?"

"Great isn't it," I agreed. "Perhaps we should just join in." Before Chris could respond a huge roll of thunder sounded not too far from where we were. Within minutes, the park, now returned to being a campsite, was empty of noisy families and full of rain, thunder and lightning. We slept through it all. Even the weather was in our favour.

Cassino was a nice place, friendly to tourists with good food and wine in abundance. We enjoyed our stay before heading for Rome.

Chris was lost in thought, as we headed for the capital, then and apropos of nothing in particular he came out with, "Italy is a nice place until you get the bill."

"Profound," I said, and would have asked more if my pillow wasn't already talking me into a few hours of total-immersion therapy.

Before I knew it, we were in Rome. Chris told me the drive had been pleasant and that we had driven along, "Winding, winding, winding, winding roads, with trees."

I thought he was simply making a joke but he wasn't. It was at that point I seriously thought that Chris might be unravelling. If I'd have had any real thought in my head, for I am a bear of little brain, I might have wondered if it had anything to do with getting closer to Britain, but I didn't. As I can barely chew gum and walk at the same time, you can understand why all other thoughts left my head as we drove past the Coliseum. I kept a look out for any stray gladiators.

Sunday is a good day to visit Rome. Little traffic, lots of parking, not too many people around and it was easy to get around this stunningly beautiful city full of dirty, filthy, stinking, thieving bastards.

We parked just around the corner from the Coliseum. We thought we ought to visit it. It was an interesting pile of bricks; we are still incredibly blasé about ancient buildings. Our thirst not quenched, we went in search of other beauty in the way only we seemed to do; a headlong rush without spending any real 'quality' time.

The Victoria Emanuel Monument, Campidoglio where racing bicycle gears come from whizzed by, we went to The Forum and the Palatine Hill, which coasted by in a blur. We have the pictures to prove it. The Pantheon had closed half an hour before we got there so we headed for the Trevi fountain; went into MacDonald's but they didn't have any root beer so came out again. We ran down the Spanish steps counting in Spanish, because we could, and headed for the Vatican, which we felt warranted us, at least, slowing to a jog.

The Vatican and St Peters, in particular, is an awesome sight.

"San Pietro in Vaticano took a hundred and twenty years to build; St Peter was supposedly crucified and buried here. A box of bones was found, cunningly hidden in a KFC box, and is now under the main altar. No one has done any tests on the bones, because it makes a nice story and the Colonel is cool with it. They bury all the popes here now so it wouldn't do to mess with tradition I guess," said Chris.

"You are becoming more cynical by the day," I said. "What other wonderful facts do you have for me?"

"Loads, but the one which you'll enjoy most is the obelisk in the middle of Pete's square, the one with the cross on top, you can't miss it, well, it's dates back to the thirteenth century before Christ and it comes from Egypt," said Chris.

"Well, that's a good laugh," I said, "because aren't they supposed to represent the sun god, Ra, or something. I remember reading something in Luxor about obelisks being frozen rays of the Sun disk . . . er . . . eaten . . . no . . . uten . . . nah . . . aten, that's it aten, the sun disk was called aten."

Chris stood with a look of mock horror on his face. "You mean to tell me that I thought you hadn't been paying attention on the whole trip when all along you've been storing information away!"

"Ha ha! Shithead!" I said. "I'll tell you something else too, Mr Smarty-pants-dog-breath-stinky-feet. The Romans were and still are infatuated with obelisks, to the extent that there are now more than twice as many obelisks standing in Rome as remain in Egypt."

"I'm impressed," said Chris. "Is that just in Rome or is that all of Italy?

"Rome," I was winging it, but felt confident.

"Herod the Great . . ." said Chris in a mock casual tone.

"As opposed to Herod the Inadequate?" I cut in quickly for the cheap laugh.

". . . set up a red granite Egyptian obelisk in the hippodrome of his grand new city Caesarea in northern Palestine you know," said Chris. "It was discovered by archaeologists and has been re-erected at its former site."

I would never beat Chris at the facts thing but it was fun testing him sometimes. His knowledge of trivia was truly awesome.

Gleaned from some of his erudition I can tell you that there is, apparently, a real piece of the cross that Jesus was nailed to inside the ball on top of the cross outside, St Peters Balalaika, it's an interesting story but would it still be there?

We looked everywhere around the Balalaika but I couldn't see any Greek people playing stringed instruments at all, otherwise I would have asked them about the piece of the true cross. We went to the toilets at the Vatican. The Cistern chapel was fragrant but they were out of paper towels, so we wiped our hands on the ceiling.

We went up into the cupola of St. Pete's too and I find this hard, in an emotional way, for me to explain. The way the sun streams in through the windows inside the cupola reminded me of when I was a child.

Driving along on sunny yet cloudy days one could see the sun beaming down through the clouds, streams of brilliant light; it used to astound me. I even asked my mother, the lapsed Catholic, if the streams of light were God. The sight inside the cupola reminded me of my childlike perception of God.

That was the big guy's chance to convert me if he was going to try it. He fluffed it by looking the other way, or he was relying on the light show to do the job. The sharp intake of breath left me feeling a little giddy. Chris was glancing sideways at me but never said a word.

We went to the Vatican museum; we even went to the gift shop, where we each bought a 'pope on a rope' the new line in ecumenical bathing products. We would soon have pious armpits to go with our Incontentia rubber underpants. We left the Vatican suitably calmed but not refreshed. We bought Fanta 'limons' from a street vendor who should have been wearing a striped shirt, a mask and carrying a bag with 'swag' written on it. Four quid for a small bottle of fizzy pope, I bet he's in for a cut.

Whilst lunging around Rome at a rate of knots one thing we did pick up was that all the chat-up lines for foreign women are the same. "Hey, baby," said hanging out of a car window or from a Lambretta seems be the classic. Women, of course, immediately want to get into bed with anyone with such winning repartee. I believe 'Oi, darlin!' works just as well in Britain when shouted from third-storey scaffolding by a hod-carrier revealing his butt crack to the world. How could a woman resist such charm?

I haven't forgotten the scathing attack on Romans in general I made a few paragraphs back. I'm getting to that - trust me.

After our whistle-stop tour of Rome, we made our way back to the car to find that one of the side glass panels had been smashed to facilitate the theft of my diving equipment and portable stereo. There were valuables all over the place but that is what they stole. Some thieving little toe-rag had made off with several thousand dollars of scuba diving equipment that would be useless in Rome. The stereo was cheap as chips and I would have given it to the thieves had they but asked. We were very upset with Rome and Romans and decided to leave as soon as we had obtained a police report for the car insurance. I have never been back to Rome and always warn people not to take anything valuable with them. I'll have to get over it one day I suppose.

The treatment from the police led me to believe they were in on the breaking and entering of my car. And, every few minutes another tourist entered the police station with something missing. In a few cases, this also involved assault and battery. It was not a side of Rome I hope you get to see; but it was a revelation. Actually, it was an eye-closer for one of the people who had been mugged for their watches. When any Monty Python fan asks me, "What have the Romans ever done for us? They are treated to a rambling vitriol-filled diatribe on why I hate Rome and Romans. I should forgive and forget but I won't just yet and you can't make me.

We went on to Viterbo to crash, as in sleep, for the night, before heading on to Pisa in the morning. We would have done a lot more in Italy. Whatever it was going to be now had to be done in sight of the Nissan. We hadn't seen another Pathfinder since we got to the country and didn't hold out much hope of finding a spare window anywhere. We would have to get something cut to shape. I wanted it to be the thieves' genitals but that was unlikely.

The Nissan was the most fantastic car for this journey. It had sailed through everything we threw at it with flying colours. It took a thief or thieves with a brick to show its one weakness. I can't tell you how upset I was. Suffice to say that I still get angry when I think about it. We had led charmed lives up to that point. It took one of the most beautiful cities in the world to spoil it. And, of course, they couldn't help me out with my dilemma, oh no! They didn't steal the Dogsbane.

In Viterbo we got drunk and slept in the car. We cursed Italy and Italians all night and then tried letting it all go in the morning. We slept off our wake for the window.

Still fuming the following day we paid a cursory visit to Pisa leaving the car covered up for a while and then decided to cut the rest of Italy from our itinerary. We started to drive to Florence but our hearts were not with Italy any more. During the day, Chris and I seemed to be talking more about England than anything else. The rot was setting in. The closer we got to England the more its emotional pull affected us.

In Pisa, we took the obligatory pictures of each of us holding the leaning tower up, or in my case pushing it over. We decided to head for France and then on to Spain.

The quickest way was by autoroute, but you have to pay cash on the darn things and we had avoided them like the plague up to that point. There was urgency in our getting out of Italy now, however.

After eventually finding a garage that took Visa, and that actually had the necessary machinery to charge the card, we took off for the French border, rapido. The funniest thing was getting on the autoroute.

We pitched up at the first booth, only to find the attendant with his back to us and he seemed to have no intention of moving. I eased the truck forward to see if the barrier was automated, it was not. I backed up and honked the horn. It took a couple of seconds for the attendant to wake up and face us. He had the most wonderful comedic moustache that he was actually wiggling from side to side as if he was gargling or something. He could easily have been a baddy from a black and white silent movie.

"Can we go through?" I asked.

In a voice, that any pantomime dame would be proud of, he said, in English, "First you push the button, then you get a ticket and thh-heeeennn you can go through."

I wanted to shout, "Behind you," but what I really shouted was: "Arrivederci, mate, I will not be back here in a hurry." It must have bothered him a lot because he turned around and went straight back to sleeping on the job.

Before we knew it, we were in France and heading for a place named after the famous casual clothes designer, Francois Mynnthe-Gap.

Chapter Seventeen

In March 1815, on his way back to Elba, Napoleon stopped in Gap, not to buy clothes, but to sleep for the night. The place has never looked back. Tens of people stop there overnight but instead of going to Elba, they ski in the winter or mill around wondering what they are doing there.

The town of Gap is the main urban centre in the upper Alps. It is a capital with a particularly pleasant natural setting with high mountains all around. Located between the Provence and Dauphiné regions (that's not the Miami Dauphinés by the way), it has a temperate climate at an altitude of 750 m, which to two hard-nosed travellers is highly intoxicating and soporific.

(Sung to the tune of '24-hours from Tulsa') Oh, we were only twenty-four hours from Dover, ah, only one day away from its charms. The jukebox started to play and night time turned into day, as we were drinkin', heav'ly, all of a sudden, we lost control as Gap showed it charms. And it caressed us, kissed us, told us we'd die before it would just let us go. Oh, we were only twenty-four hours from Dover . . .

With karaoke out of our systems, we found a great little hotel where the owner, a flirtatious forty-something, in fine fettle and who obviously liked Englishmen, a rarity anywhere in France. She told us of her gastronomic festival that was running in the hotel coupled with some wonderful and reasonable promotions on local wines. It was love, or at least lush, at first sight.

You can ski in Gap in the winter or walk around a bit, eat, and drink a lot in summer. We were definitely there at the right time. And Fifi, not her real name, was an exceptional host. She wore a French maid's outfit like no one I had ever seen, just kidding, or am I? As there were not many guests in the hotel, she was making the most of the few she had. Her late-night room service was unbelievable.

"You would like some 'ot chocolate to take wiz you to bed?"

"If it was anything like last night, Fifi, I don't think one will be enough," I said puffing out my chest.

"You are a naughty boy to tease Fifi so." She oozed sexiness and it was seemingly effortless.

"Do you think she's really up for it, or is she just having us on?" asked Chris as Fifi moved on to talk with other guests.

"I dunno, Chris, what do you think? I said, lecherously watching her walk away. "Maybe you'll find out later: I recommend the hot chocolate on the room-service menu, by the way."

We made telephone calls, caught up on journals and swam in the pool by day. We didn't need to eat during the day, as the one meal per day was more than enough. The smallest was eleven courses and we were consuming anywhere from two to I don't know how many bottles of wine at night. We talked off and on. Chris was definitely nervous about getting back to the UK but we never got any further than that. I had resigned myself (again) to delivering the Dogsbane to my father. Surely, if I ignored the problem it would go away.

We played golf one day but it was a mistake. I believe the course was designed with mountain goats in mind and said as much to Chris. This triggered a hidden joke in the darkest recesses of my mind handed down over the centuries and told by generation after generation in my family. Learning the joke and telling it to other family members was a rite of passage for all members of the Hunt clan. Today, for the first time ever I will share our family's secret heritage with you.

"I know a man who keeps goats in his bedroom," I said to Chris who is not slow on the uptake.

On cue he replied, "A man who keeps goats in his bedroom, what about the smell?"

"Oh, the goats don't mind." The funniest thing about old jokes like this is that they are so old and so well-known that one cannot help but laugh.

The views from our Alpine golf course were stunning but the golf was awful. We blamed the altitude for making our balls go everywhere, it seemed, but where we wanted them to go. Still, if you are going to play golf badly there are few nicer places, I imagine.

We went into town, found a launderette, and did our washing. Found some Perspex the right thickness at an art shop and the proprietor cut it to shape for us. Our number one priority, the window, was suitably fixed. After a few days of pigging out and sleeping with the hotel owner, we decided to move on. Chris foolishly didn't take me up on the hot chocolate suggestion. Fifi made the last night special, the food was incredible, she recommended all the wines for us and then sat with us for brandies.

The next day we bought groceries and repacked the truck in readiness to set off for Orange, which would be the next stop on Greg and Chris's Great Adventure. Well, we have been to a number of important Catholic places so we had to visit at least one important Protestant place for the sake of balance. William the Silent (not made up) or William of Orange, the first Stadtholder of the Orange province inherited the place along with his silver spoon. A devout Protestant he kicked some serious Catholic butt in his time. The town of Orange these days is controversial in its outlook. It is the flagship and stronghold of the Front National even the mayor is of that party. Coincidence?

Orange is renowned for its Roman architecture; it possesses the best-preserved Roman theatre in Europe, as well as a particularly fine triumphal arch where the Roman fighting force '2 Gallica' are commemorated, both edifices were built during the reign of Augustus. You remember him; he had a month named after him.

Being in France after Italy was a shock; the two Nationalities were so different. I found the Italians despicably rude, arrogant and generally unfriendly. I found the French wonderfully polite, humble and friendly. Now as an Englishman, and it is necessary for me to make that distinction from Britons, that was horrifying. We English are bred to hate the French; it is genetically imprinted on our souls. We have hated the French for centuries, they hate us and that's the way of the world. We are an island race and they are the nearest people to us so it is only natural that we hate them. I was perturbed.

"Chris, we hate the French – why are they being so nice to us?" I asked. "Is it a trick?"

"Ah ha!" said Chris in a most uncharacteristically pantomimic way. "These are the southern French and not as spiky and hateful as the northern French who have to put up with our drunken louts invading them periodically," he said. "Don't fret, you would still hate Parisians, trust me on that."

"I was getting a little worried, you know. I didn't realise we hate the Italians as well," I said with my inherent racism and island-bred genes coming to the fore.

"Never fear," said Chris. "The English hate everyone, but the French, the northern French even more than everyone else."

"I did not feel welcome in Italy and I do in France, the Italians have no manners; French manners are impeccable. I hate Italy."

"Here is something to debate at your next dinner party, when you are not freaking the hell out of everyone by talking about euthanasia, ask your guests to name a country whom the English, and their cohorts, over time, haven't invaded, fought with or tried to rape, pillage or colonise," said Chris.

"There must be plenty, surely," I said.

"First of all, don't call me Shirley, second of all, name one," said Chris.

"Ah, China," I said.

"Opium wars," said Chris.

"Australia," I said as my only operational brain cell whizzed around my empty skull bumping into itself.

"A good guess, and we haven't had a war with them, but we did dump all our convicts there, so they have been colonised by our detritus, and a jolly good job of it they've made too," he said in an Australian accent.

"Bloody hell it's not easy is it, how about Switzerland?"

"A good choice and an easy target if I may be so bold, but in 1500 BC Celts, whom I would consider cohorts to the English, but they may not, settled the area now known as Switzerland," said Chris. "Care to try for today's star prize, the blow on the head?"

"I go to church regularly," I said in a screechy voice and joining in with the Monty Python sketch. Chris had been a big fan too.

"Jolly good! Well now, madam, your first question for the blow on the head this evening is: Which great opponent of Cartesian dualism resists the reduction of psychological phenomena to a physical state and insists there is no point of contact between the extended and the unextended?

"I don't know that."

"Well . . . have a guess!"

"Oh... Henri Bergson"

" ...is the correct answer!" shouted Chris enthusiastically.

"Ooh, that was lucky. I never even heard of him," I said, and then laughed. We stopped the sketch there and sat quietly for a minute, and then I added, "You're right, I can't think of one country we haven't had some kind of trouble with. That's a damning indictment of our little island, eh what?"

We drove along the wine route toward Orange, we couldn't think of anything we really wanted to do there, so carried on to D'Avignon. After looking at the Pont, we thought we'd carry on to Montpellier as we might well have somewhere to stay there thanks to friends of ours in Abu Dhabi. They were on holiday.

So, at 6:55 pm on Saturday, August 31, with two weeks left until we were supposed to meet up with my now former girlfriend from Abu Dhabi, Hannah, in Barcelona for my birthday, bored with travelling, France and everything else, we turned north and headed for Calais, the trip was almost over and tomorrow we would be in England.

The car was running well, we had some petrol in the tank and even some in the spare tank. The window had been repaired and we were set for a long drive. Well, a long drive to some, after all, we had just driven from the Middle East. There was cockiness in the way we talked of driving hundreds or even thousands of kilometres.

We repacked the Nissan, for what was probably the last time, so that the passenger seat could recline fully. Passengers were allowed to sleep and drivers were not. We had come too far to end up as a French statistic.

This was it . . . we were heading . . . er . . . home. Abu Dhabi seemed a million miles away.

After our initial excitement at this change in our travel plans, we fell silent as the realisation set in. Any conversation now would have been forced, so with music in the background, we sat without talking and feeling more like a part of the truck than a passenger did.

A couple of hundred kilometres from Paris we decided to fill up with petrol. That would see us through to Calais. Heading to the cash desk I said, "Chris, do you want anything to eat or drink or did those fifteen Mars Bars hit the spot?"

Either he wanted one of something or his middle finger gesture was plain rude. I decided not to get him anything. I greeted the cashier, "Bonsoir."

He returned the pleasantry and took my Visa for the swiping ritual. The machine rejected it immediately. He tried again and it failed again. He scrutinised the card closely and told me in broken English that it was out of date. It was 3:00 am on September 1. The card ran out on August 31. We could have filled up three hours and one minute ago on this card but now we could not.

It wasn't too worrying as I had other cards. Except that is that by some quirk of fate my other Visa ran out on August 31 too. I took the trusty Gold American Express Card out of its holster and pointed it at the attendant.

He said, "Non."

Bugger, they didn't take Amex. Now what? I would have to talk with Chris and went for the door, the attendant said, "Monsieur?" I don't think he liked the idea of me leaving without paying. Flustered at this turn of events I said, "Ein minute, bitte." Realising that I had a touch of linguistic continental drift I resorted to the Arabic sign of all one's fingertips meeting upside down with a gentle rocking movement, which means 'ein minute bitte' or something to that effect. It's a universal gesture. Luckily, French petrol attendants don't care what language you speak as long as you pay.

I brought Chris up to speed. We had 350 Francs in cash, which was to pay our autoroute bill and any other emergencies. Our current outstanding petrol bill was Fr 320. We had to use up our cash and work out something for the autoroute. Knowing our good fortune, something always turns up. Trust me it is not easy being that cavalier.

We left that service station with Fr 30 between us. We decided to stop at the next service station to work out a solution to our problem that may involve illegally getting off the autoroute.

Chris started searching around for money or wire cutters. I believe he may have been whistling the theme tune of the Great Escape.

At the next service station, we drove in slowly looking for service exits and the like. This was not something we liked the idea of but we couldn't get any more money while we were on the autoroute and no one was going to let us leave it to go and get more.

We had another coffee because we were only hopped up to the eyeballs with caffeine. We wanted it coming out of our ears. Gnashing our teeth and chewing the inside of our cheeks like speed freaks, Chris opened up our money pouch again and brought out what we had both thought were empty traveller cheque vouchers.

As we had been changing mostly dollars during the trip, we had forgotten the Sterling traveller's cheques. Inside the voucher sat a GBP 50 traveller's cheque. We were saved again from becoming fugitives from the law. The guy in the garage changed it for us and we got a better rate than we'd been getting from Fifi. There's no such thing as a free lunch I guess.

Chris in his usual efficient manner searched the car from top to bottom for cash after that. We had some Egyptian pounds, some Italian Lira; I had some Austrian Schillings for some reason and an assortment of Drachma finished off our collection. Notes and coins totalled about GBP 4.61.

"In my wallet Chris, there is a one dollar bill, if we are really desperate, I don't know why I have that but I'll throw it into the pot if necessary. I guess with it being Sunday we are not going to be able to get any cash."

"We'll do fine, the only question mark now is Calais and Amex, which will not be a problem," he said.

We now had enough money for the autoroute, we had a full tank and we were confident that the ferry terminal would take Amex. Why Chris didn't have any credit cards I don't know but I had only just thought of it after two months of putting everything on my cards. We would total up and split the difference in the next few days, and, go our separate ways - how bizarre that thought seemed. Chris and I were joined at the hip these days.

Approaching Paris, we decided to try to listen out for an English radio station and this is where I got the working title for this book, which was not They Saddle Dogs but Losing My Religion.

Letting the radio search for itself, it came to an English radio station playing REM's remarkable track. We had heard this on Abu Dhabi radio as we left the UAE. My good friend Tim who was a DJ at that time played it for us. We had heard it in various places in Egypt including the 'Disco bar' in Mursa Mutruh. I'm sure Michael Stipe, the singer and front man with REM and his band mates would be impressed with the reach of the song. We heard it in Crete, repeatedly. We heard it in Italy on an American forces radio station we listened to while in Monte Cassino. Here we were in France dashing for Dover and we heard it again. It was quite weird. It was great as a focus for writing this book. I am listening to it right now.

The radio station faded and we searched again and found another English language station. You know what it was playing so I won't go into any more slightly spooky details. We just had to accept it. Michael Stipe was stalking us, which would also have been a good title for the book.

We reached Calais without any further ado.

"Do you take American Express?" I asked in the ticket office.

"That'll do nicely, sir," the cashier said aping the famous American Express advertisements and obviously not tired of saying the same thing day-in and day-out for years on end. "You just got here in time for the first ferry to England, where are you travelling from?"

Chris and I smiled at one another and then said, "Abu Dhabi in the Middle East."

"Wow, how long did that take?" asked the cashier.

"Two months to the day," I said, looking at my expired Visa cards.

The ferry trip went smoothly and without any hitch. There were no Egyptian lorry drivers to be found anywhere and the tea and coffee prices were exorbitant but no one tried to throw the staff overboard. We were back in civilisation and I immediately felt depressed as the weight of what I had to face crept over me like someone placing a wet blanket around my shoulders.

We landed in Dover hungry and tired yet eager to get going to Melbourne. Chris had cued up REM to be the first track we heard as we landed in England. I liked his style.

The Customs procedures at Dover were far more involved than any we had been through; it was reassuring in a way. When they saw our Middle Eastern identification, we were immediately taken to one side for special treatment. There's nothing like a bit of racial stereotyping to start the day. We had come from the Middle East and therefore needed to be searched more than anyone else is. The fact that we were obviously English or British had nothing to do with it.

They were thorough. They looked underneath the car, they looked for loose panels and anywhere that contraband could be stored. They even moved the Dogsbane to one side so that they could look all the way into the jack compartment. They found nothing of interest. I laughed aloud and one of the Customs officers gave me a funny look.

"I have Tourettes syndrome," I said looking him square in the face and visually daring him to question me further. He nodded as if he understood. He was not intimidated but he backed away from me nevertheless.

We repacked our stuff, which probably really was the last time. We had been with Customs a while.

Chris said, "I am famished." I knew just the place for us to go.

Just outside of Dover, we found the Happy Eater where I was going to dump Chris's body had he not turned out to be such a star. We ordered an all-day breakfast or whatever it is called and wolfed it down in minutes. The young, inexperienced and ever so pleasant waitress said, "Is there anything else I can get you?"

Chris smiled and then said to her, "Same again please."

She laughed and said, "Sure . . . is there really anything else I can get you?"

"Sure," said Chris. "The same again please."

And, we ate our way through the same meal again, with piles of bread and butter and mugs of steaming hot coffee watched closely by the Happy Eater staff. They gave us a round of applause as we finished with two clean plates, an unfastening of belts and top buttons. It was amusing to be back in England, YouKay.

We drove to Melbourne with plenty of people staring at us once they saw the Arabic 'Hexport Playtsh' that had caused us so many paperwork problems but by doing that contributed to the adventure. My friends who lived in Melbourne, Liz and Steve, whom I had rung from the road in France, had put some milk in the fridge and the bare necessities such as tea and coffee. The phone had already been reconnected in readiness for my return supposedly in a few weeks and the beds were made up. Chris and I would have our own rooms tonight.

We spent the day telephoning family and friends, especially Hannah, as I didn't want her to head off to Barcelona. Our families were all pleased and relieved that we were back safe and when would we be going to visit.

I made the last entry in to my tape recorder with the promise that some details would be filled in. They never were. The last word on side seven of tapes euphemistically titled 'The Journey Home' was 'anon'.

Chris left the following day to go and see his family. He was agitated and had cut himself several times shaving it seemed. What I didn't know at the time was that he had shaved repeatedly and that the cuts were because of that. His stress levels were off the charts now he was back in the country which caused his angst. I didn't see it.

I went about the business of building some form of life for myself in the UK. I had a trip to Montana to plan to see an old girlfriend who was studying medicine there. I also needed to see another old girlfriend, great how we're still all friends, who had called and wanted to meet straight away, she was heavily into the spiritual scene. She dabbled a lot with Tarot cards and other much stranger stuff. The reason we had split up was that it was all getting a little too weird for me, and this would be no exception.

Portia was tall and willowy with long black hair and pale skin. She had the Gothic look off to a tee without wearing make-up. She came to my house and was breathless with the story she had to tell me. A story that was about me and went like this . . .

* * *

"I had been having trouble sleeping and as is often the way I found myself thinking of you. When I did drift into sleep, I was having the strangest nightmares, which involved you. She laughed. "Anyway, the dreams got bad and the lack of sleep was starting to affect my health so I went to see my friend Michael, the Shaman. He said that you were the cause and that your spirit was in conflict with mine."

I could feel my eyes rolling at this point and my head starting to spin round and around, it would not be long before I started spewing green goo and other such pleasantries. "Portia, is this going anywhere?" I asked.

"Be patient, my love," she said, "this will be worth putting up with me for a while, trust me."

She continued: "Michael told me this, and I swear I gave him no information, he said that you, he didn't know who you were, were travelling in Egypt and that your spirit was 'attacking' mine. It was some karmic debt from thousands of years ago that had not been resolved and that your soul was in torment."

"Oh, I'm a soul in torment all right," I said. "When was this that he said I was travelling in Egypt?"

"It was . . . let me see . . . August, no, no, July. It was July the eighth about midday, I had just finished doing a reading for my mother," she said. The date and time put me in the Valley of the Kings. "Greg, if that wasn't spooky enough Michael insisted on going into trance there and then, I've never seen him do that before."

"So what else came out of this happy occasion with the 'trancing' Michael and the spookily beautiful Portia?" I asked trying not to show my agitation.

Portia then detailed what Michael said he could see, "He said there were white men and Arab men. You were one of the white men, I guess. One Arab was happy and helping you with something, the other was begging or trying to steal from you. You didn't like the thief and were going to hurt him but the other white man stopped you. The thief said to you 'Are you angry English'? Does this mean anything to you?"

I was shaking; she had just described exactly the situation in the Valley of Kings with Abdul Rahman, Chris and the temple guard who had tried to rip us off and ripped up our tickets instead. "Portia, what does this mean then?" I asked.

"Is it true then, did that happen?" she asked.

"Only to the letter, Portia, only to the letter," I could feel the hairs on the back of my neck doing the Bossa Nova.

"Cool, I'll have to tell Michael that. Anyway he guided your spirit to a safe place and you'll be all right for now, as will I, well, for a couple of hundred years maybe, but you're going to have to sort this karmic debt thing out with me at some point."

"I'd like to meet this Michael," I said still more than a little shaken.

"Yeah! He said you'd say that. He also said you can't meet him just yet but he would get in touch with you when, and if, the time was right," she said.

""I remember why we split up now, you scare me shitless," I said. "I can't tell anyone this story either because no one would believe me. You've freaked me out just so you can check your weird friend's accuracy - thanks a lot."

Portia stayed for tea and told me what she was doing with her life. I have to confess I didn't really listen and I think she saw the detached look on my face and stood to leave.

She bent to kiss me and then stopped, taking in a small sharp breath.

I looked at her and her face was ashen, "When you go and see your father make your peace with him."

"Don't say another word, Portia, you've said enough today," I said now feeling animosity toward her.

She hugged me and kissed me on the cheek and whispered, "It's all going to be fine, don't worry." As she walked down the drive to her Porsche, which I have always thought was funny, she sang, "That's me in the corner, that's me in the spotlight . . .

Why would I be surprised?

I needed to think all this stuff through. Or did I? It was too weird to think about. I had enough on my plate. I would deal with it in a couple of hundred years. But, slightly more pressingly I had to go and see my father and take him his Dogsbane.

In my life, I have always talked over any problems with my sisters. The younger of the two Jackie, more than Lynn, who lived in Cornwall. Jackie and I were closer in years and Lynn had left home when I was 12 so there was a natural gap. My sisters, I feel, brought me up more than my parents did, especially my big sister Lynn. She had always called me 'my baby'. But here I was facing the biggest dilemma of my life and I couldn't talk to them about it. Whatever happened I hoped they would understand. If my father decided to use the Dogsbane, I would have to tell them after the fact and explain why. That, or cop the fifth I believe my American wife might have said. The trouble with that being that Britain doesn't have a fifth amendment and silence is not always golden.

Driving along the A1M and then the M25 towards Watford, where my father lived, I looked at the bag in the footwell of the passenger seat where the Dogsbane sat growling and slavering. I felt I was settled with it, but now was the time to be face to face with my father.

Chapter Eighteen

The house where my father and his second wife, Ann, live is the house where I grew up. I thought I would have strong emotions about that, but didn't. Everything seemed smaller and less colourful as I drove the Nissan into Acacia Copse, which is a cul-de-sac. I didn't feel as if I was coming home.

Other than my father's house, nothing looked familiar in the street. The garden of the house was unkempt and strewn with unfinished projects. Parked on the drive was Ann's blue Lada, or was it a skip? Next to that was my father's white elephant. It was a slow mode of transport but it drew many admiring glances and was good for the flowers. It wasn't really white or an elephant. It was a camper van that the rest of the family called the 'Chip Van'.

My father had always loved travelling around Britain. When I was young, we camped and hiked; as my father aged, he ungraciously gave in to having one or two creature comforts, such as a bed, a toilet and a cooking stove that didn't need a degree in applied engineering to light. He was a purist, but he gave into a camper van, that you could have sold chips from without too much imagination.

The greeting with Ann was always frosty on my part. She loved my father and looked after him but rubbed me up the wrong way every time. She had expected to be called Mum by my sisters, and me, which was laughable considering her age. She also demanded respect via our father. We felt she had to earn it and as that was unlikely; she would be kept at arm's length.

Before even saying 'hello', Ann asked me what was in the bag.

"Nothing of interest to you," I said rudely, then added, "It's just cleaning products," hoping this would keep her at bay. "Is my father up?" I called out to her as she retreated.

"You can go straight up, he's been waiting for your visit," she said, sneaking a sideways glance at my bag before she disappeared along the filthy, book-lined hallway. Ann was not house-proud. In fact, I don't think Ann knew what housework was, she 'enjoyed' poor health and at one time or another had had every complaint my father had and more. It must be galling to her that he has trumped her with real stomach cancer - how can one beat that?

Everything in the house was coated with grime as it had been pretty much since my mother left. Not that my mother was the Mother Theresa of housekeeping but this filth was disgusting and probably not good for my father's health. My sisters had tried to intervene, had tried to get the local authorities involved but had been stopped by our father. They had to let it go.

When I saw my father lying on top of his bed, he appeared as if he had shrunk. His hair had grown long, was totally silver and he was dressed in a frock-like nightshirt. His beard was unkempt and his skin was pale, blotchy and waxy. This was not the man I had nearly come to blows with over the physical way he had treated my mother. He seemed like a strong breeze would blow him away.

"Hi, Dad," I said as jauntily as I could manage, "I love what you've done with the place. And your hair is interesting, does it take long to manage in the morning or do you just stick your head into the hedge?"

"Don't start, dear boy, I don't have the strength to joust with you," he said, his voice every bit as strong as I remembered it. I reverted to the naughty but headstrong six-year-old who refused to take one of the beatings he used to dish out with a leather strap.

Rather than prevaricating, which was not our way, I said, "Have you any god-damned idea how much aggravation you caused me with that bloody plant sap escapade?"

He laughed and coughed at the same time as if they were inextricably linked to one another. "Been causing you some trouble has it?" he said, once he was able.

"Not as much as you'd probably like, you twisted old goat, but I have had more than my share of sleepless nights," I said using the intimidation in my speech and manner I had learned from him over the years. I could hear Ann starting to move around outside the door and dropped my voice. "The witch was trying to stick her beak in my bag when I came in."

Calling Ann the witch caused my father to wince and I felt guilty. He would be on his own or in a home if it weren't for her. I felt a home would be better and total torture for my father, which undoubtedly he deserved. He hated mixing with anyone from the real world. His various illnesses had caused him to withdraw almost totally.

"Well, dear boy, you are going to hate me even more than you did before, because I'm no longer going to need that stuff after all," he said.

"You have got to be joking, you bloody fraud – are you telling me that you're not dying now and I went through sodding purgatory for nothing?" I was almost crying with rage as all my emotions shot to the surface. What I had been put through mentally over the last two months was something I couldn't have done to anyone. That evil son-of-a-bitch was going to cheat death again. That is if I didn't kill him right then and there, with my bare hands. It wouldn't take much from the look of him.

"You'll have to be a man, my son," he said in that awful pompous way of his, "I am going to die rather sooner than we all expected. The cancer has spread and this old bag of bones I have euphemistically called a body doesn't have any fight left. The upside of that is I am allowed, pretty much, all the drugs I want. The Dogsbane is too much effort for very little reward."

"Jesus Christ, Dad, I'm so sorry. I've been so wrapped up in my own worries that didn't even cross my mind," I said in an emotional about face. No matter how negative my feelings were about him, facing him at that point would have softened the hardest heart.

The Dogsbane that had travelled thousands of miles was already history and I could only guess at how far I had been prepared to go with euthanasia from then on.

"I would have said exactly the same thing so don't worry about it," he said. "I'm sorry if I caused you a lot of trouble and anguish, although you probably needed a nudge to grow up a little and start taking some responsibility."

"I would shut your pie-hole, old man, because you just had my sympathy and in true Raymond Charles Maurice Hunt style you blew it."

I choked some tears back because I realised I was never going to be six ever again. I wasn't going to be able to curse him out for making us do things the hard way and he was never going to be able to stand up for me against the rest of the world no matter how wrong I was, which was probably the best trait I could think of about him.

"Don't cry for me, I haven't been a very good father and who knows perhaps you'll learn from that, and look at it this way: I get all the morphine I want now. I'm just like an airport . . . terminal."

"Now I know you're dying," I said, barely keeping a handle on my emotions. "You've never made a joke in your life . . . mind you, you still haven't."

I felt so alone. My father, even at that stage of his life, was able to keep me at a distance with his words and attitude. I was convinced he did love me; he wasn't able to show it, which for me wasn't enough. I needed hugs, assurances and support. My father would have seen that as a weakness and wouldn't know how to respond. He couldn't be demonstrative with affection and by return I wasn't allowed to show it either. I think if I had hugged him, he might have crumbled into dust.

After we talked a while longer, and he had wound me up to the point where I really did want to kill him, I decided it was time to leave. I touched his pasty-white, shiny hand and said, "See you on the other side, old man, and you'd better be waiting for me because I'm going to kick your butt."

"I don't doubt that for one second. I've often thought you had more than your fair share of thuggish-ness," he said.

I headed out the door slowly, torn as to whether I should leave. I was about to break down in a sobbing heap when I heard his creaking voice call out, "Greg?"

I ducked my head back in the door and said, "Yes, Dad?"

"I'm sorry."

I waved good-bye because I couldn't speak. I swept down the stairs and out to the Nissan without even acknowledging Ann. I drove down Acacia Copse far too fast, stopped at the end of the road, and burst into a flood of tears. I sobbed uncontrollably for however long it was. I lost track of time but eventually made my way home in a stunned silence.

I hid away for a couple of days thinking about my life, thinking about my father's life. We were different and the same. I realised I was mourning him already and I felt resigned to it. He did not have a great life and obviously was ready to move on to the next great adventure.

My sisters kept me up to date with Dad's blood transfusions, medication and so on. I told them about the Dogsbane. They chastised me for not sharing but understood. I asked them if I had time for a two-week trip to Montana and they agreed I probably did.

I had tried getting in touch with Chris before I travelled but had no luck. The two weeks away was what I needed to get myself back on track. My old girlfriend Felicia had found herself a new man. She moved out of her apartment for me, gave me her car and we met occasionally when she could fit me in between studying and her boyfriend who was not at all happy about having an old flame on his territory.

That time in Montana was great for clearing the cobwebs away. I read a great deal. I was ready for whatever would come next in my life, even though I was going to have at least one very heavy family 'do' to attend in the not-too-distant future.

Back in Melbourne, I found a few messages on my answering machine and one was from Chris's sister. Without unpacking, I got into the Nissan and headed for Shrewsbury.

His sister and doctor wanted to ask me about what had gone on during the trip. I told them everything and the doctor retold it to me from Chris's perspective. Chris had had some sort of a breakdown and he was quite heavily sedated. Apparently, many issues needed dealing with but he was reluctant to face them. Getting closer and closer to his issues, or getting back to the UK in our situation, had wound him tighter than he could cope with and he had retreated to a place of safety. The doctor assured us that with rest, medication and care he would be back in shape in no time.

I stayed for a few days but it was obvious that he needed his family and not a travelling companion around. I visited him whenever his sister thought it appropriate. He is now well and working as a civil engineer and living as peaceful and stress-free life as he can. We still speak from time to time on the phone, over a beer or through email. We don't talk about the trip and we don't talk about his stress-related problems and it seems we're both fine with that. Why deal with reality if you don't have to?

Time marched on. I got the Nissan registered for full-time use on British roads and gradually got used to driving a left-hand drive car in a right-hand drive country. Overtaking was interesting but certainly no more threatening than driving from Cairo to Luxor.

One morning as I was about to leave for a book shopping trip in Cambridge I received a nasty shock, one that I wasn't expecting.

Leaving the house and going through all my necessary rituals of checking doors and windows at least twice, making sure everything was turned off, then going back upstairs to check one last time, I closed the front door firmly behind me. Turning to walk down the drive to the Nissan, I was confronted with an empty space where it was supposed to be.

I checked the garage, which was at the back of the house; to see if I'd put it away. I went back in the house wondering if I had left it somewhere before the realisation hit me. It had been stolen. I dug out all the nice new documents the government had given me for the truck and called the police. In a rather bored manner, they took all of my details and said they'd get back to me if they heard anything.

The outstanding Nissan, the real hero of the "Michael Stipe Is Stalking Me' tour had been taken away, for who knows what. Hopefully it would only be joy riders and with a couple of dents or even scratches and soon we would be back on the road.

I dusted off my bicycle and started using that wherever I could. Sadly, it would be for longer than I expected. A few days later, I got a call from Cambridgeshire police.

"Mr Hunt," said the woman on the telephone.

"Yes," I said.

"This is Cambridgeshire police."

"Have you found my car?"

"Yes, we have."

"That's fantastic."

"Well, no, it's not."

"Oh don't tell me they smashed it into something," I said, wondering how bad it could be, when the woman took on a much more sombre tone.

"I'm sorry to have to tell you this . . ."

"You sound as if someone has died and you're giving me the bad news," I said.

"Well, fortunately no one has died, sir," she said a little more upbeat, "but the only way we were able to recognise your car was from the chassis number," she told me with genuine sadness in her voice

"What?" I said, "I don't understand."

"Sir we believe your car may have been used in a ram raid and then set on fire to cover up any clues the perpetrators may have left behind," she said in what sounded like a rehearsed speech.

"Oh bloody hell," I said, "I don't believe it, after all that car has been through to end up being used for a robbery and then torched. That is appalling."

"The local police will be in touch with you, sir, to sort out the details," the woman said.

They came and took a statement. One of the officers brought me a number plate. You could only just make out that it was a number plate. It was burnt to a crisp. I got on to my insurance company as I had a claim pending with them for my stolen diving equipment.

The value of the Nissan in the UK was much higher than it was in the Middle East. What I bought for about ten thousand dollars was worth nearly thirteen thousand pounds. However, every claim over ten thousand had to be investigated by one of the insurance company's investigators. He made an appointment to come and see me.

To say this chap was rude would be an understatement. I had never been made to feel so guilty in my life. He virtually accused me of setting fire to my own car, without reference to any ram raids of course and insisted I write another statement for him. I was not happy with this chappy.

"I have given the police a statement already," I said.

"The police know nothing, I used to be one," he said in a most belligerent manner.

I had had enough of this guy. "I have told you all I'm going to tell you, I find your manner obnoxious and I will be making a complaint to your employers and the insurance ombudsman." I knew a little about the insurance business because my brother-in-law worked in the industry. "And you, you rude, arrogant prig, can do any further talking while you are walking - out of my house."

"If you don't give me a statement you won't get paid out," he said as if he'd lost a little wind from his sails.

"We'll see about that," I said slamming the door on his retreating figure.

I went to the insurance company's offices that day and went ballistic. I threatened them with newspapers, ombudsmen and everything else I could think of. I had them so flustered they offered to cut me a cheque there and then for the value of the Nissan. They had to write two cheques because they were not allowed to write cheques over ten thousand pounds.

I was sad to lose the Nissan; it had been the most reliable and trusty of travelling companions. We had been through a lot together, but I had travelled 10,000 kilometres from Abu Dhabi to Melbourne over a two-month period, not including any driving around I had done prior to or subsequent to the trip, and had made the equivalent of about US$ 15,000 profit. If it had to go, it had definitely gone out in style.

I banked the money, feeling good about the world, until I got home to find my sister Jackie waiting in the drive. Steve and Liz had said I was on my way back home. Jackie told me our father had died the previous night.

We cried together as only siblings can. We drank copious quantities of tea as only the British can. I travelled back with her to North London so that we could be together and get ready for what was going to be the weirdest, most uncomfortable funeral either of us would ever attend. Sadly, it was our father's, who art in H . . . er . . . well . . . we're not sure actually.

The entourage was kept small with a few select and strong-stomached members of the family. My father's wishes were that he be buried with no religious service, in a biodegradable coffin with no headstone. These do not appear to be unseemly requests; one could almost applaud such a stance. Almost.

Our cousin Gina and her husband, John, were invited, my sisters and their husbands and one tenacious niece, Holly. No friends, and not simply because they were thin on the ground, and, as he hadn't worked for many years, there would be no work colleagues. A motley little crew.

My brothers-in-law, Graham and David, had already been roped in for a particularly nasty piece of work for which, thankfully, Ann hadn't called me. The day before the funeral, I was in Melbourne whilst my brothers-in-law under the cover of darkness were moving my father's body to the Chip Van. It doesn't sound a particularly nasty job but then allow me to fill in some detail.

After my father had been signed off as dead and a death certificate issued, Ann had decided not to use professional help with the body, so it lay in state, on the bed, without any treatment, slowly decaying until the day it had to be moved to the Chip Van.

Graham and David at least didn't have to put the body into its cardboard box, someone had already done that but they did have to move the cardboard box, and that truly is what it was, to the Chip Van; downstairs, out of the door, and down the garden path to where the van awaited.

Now the following is second-hand news but I trust my brothers-in-law implicitly so know that there is no exaggeration on their part.

The bottom of the box was damp from the fluids emanating from my dead father. The stench was as close to being unbearable as it could be; both men admit to retching profusely. Graham found some Vicks Vapour Rub in the bathroom and both of them put it up their noses to save them from smelling anything else. Graham swears he learned that from watching Silence of the Lambs from when they are autopsying a murdered victim who had been dead for some time.

They manhandled the box to the stairs and David being the bigger of the two went first. Everything was going OK until the box, which was not of the strongest construction, started to sag in the middle. Both men told the next piece of dialogue to me while I was getting them drunk a few days later. I have used little artistic licence and you will soon see why.

"The box is starting to go in the middle, Dave," said Graham.

"Let's just keep going and try and get it to the van."

"It's going to go, we'll have to put it down," Graham said emphatically.

As David looked up to see the state of play the box sagged in the middle and one of my father's arms flopped out as if ready for a handshake.

"Oh, Jesus Christ," said David. "Now what do we do?"

"You'll have to put that back in the box, mate, I can't touch it. I'm freaking out now," said Graham.

"Let's set it down at the bottom of the stairs . . . where the hell is Ann, she could put the arm back in," said David.

"She's in the garden avoiding this I imagine," said Graham.

They set the box down and the arm flopped back in on its own just as easily as it had come out. Graham got an old piece of wood from outside to put under the box to strengthen it. They didn't want any repeats of arms being outstretched.

"Do we have to do this at night?" asked David, "Don't answer that, silly question."

"Come on let's get this done," said Graham. They lifted the box now strengthened by the wood and carried it down the garden path to put it into the Chip Van. David had already unlocked the door in preparation for the box.

David put his end onto the van and then helped Graham slide it in, up to a point. The van wasn't long enough to take the whole box.

"I do not believe this, are we on Candid Camera or something, no, no one could be this cruel. Not even Greg would set us up for this nightmare," said David.

"He should be doing this, not us, shit, what do we do now?" said Graham.

"We'll have to put it in on a tilt; I'm not getting into any more with this thing tonight. That will have to do," said David.

At that point, one of the neighbourhood mutts turned up because of the smell. Both men had had enough and were totally stressed out. A toe from one of them assisted the dog in making its mind up that being there was not a good idea.

David went to tell Ann that they had done the deed and were leaving. Apparently, she never even said thank you or any other word, well, what did she have to be chatty about? Her husband was dead, he'd been slowly decomposing in one of the bedrooms for a couple of days, it stank, and tomorrow she would have to drive the Chip Van, with the decaying corpse of her husband to the cemetery. Even I felt sorry for her after thinking that one through.

I felt sorry that is until I heard that my father had a bell he used to ring when he needed help during his illness. The night he died, he was obviously in distress and therefore ringing the bell quite a bit. She took it away from him. The only thing that sounded promising about that night was that Ann said he kept talking about seeing his sister, Doris. If I were religious, I'd thank God for that, because I'm sure he must have felt very scared and very alone.

The next day arrived soon enough. David and Graham at that point hadn't given any details, but had worked out with John and me that we would be pallbearers. I'm glad I didn't know anything else at that stage.

Gina and John had arrived early and parked their car in a nearby hotel, where they had a coffee. Leaving the car there and taking the short walk John apparently pointed out a hooker on her way into the crematorium.

Gina apparently said, "Well everyone has to be buried or cremated, why not hookers; anyway Uncle Ray would appreciate sharing his funeral with a bunch of hookers." As they entered the grounds they were amazed to see hordes of men and women all dressed in a similar gaudy over-the-top kind of way.

The women weren't hookers. All of the people there were travellers, or as my father would have called them 'Gyp-os'. The women obviously thought the height of class was to wear skirts not much longer than a belt with leather strapped shoes where the straps went up above the knee. The men were wearing gaudy suits, some with ties and others without. The children were dressed up to look older and in the girls' cases more 'tart-like'. There were hundreds of them all driving new cars, such as Mercedes and BMWs and all bearing Danish number plates for some reason known only to them. The Irish accents completed the ensemble nicely.

We tried keeping separate from the travellers but it wasn't easy as there were so many of them and when Ann turned into the cemetery in the Chip Van, wearing a scarf as a mask and having all the van windows open because of the stench, all hell broke loose. People were pointing and shouting, Traveller children were hanging on the side of the van to try to look inside, and it was bedlam. All we could do was look as she drove toward us. The crowd obviously thought the way Ann was dressed was disrespectful, but then they had no idea.

When she pulled up the huge crowd was becoming unruly and voicing their own concerns about health and safety. Some of them were shouting out that it was disgusting because the smell quite clearly told everyone what was in the van.

"Come on let's get this over with," said David. However, the crowd was starting to get in the way and even jostling. It was at this point petite and wonderful Holly blew a gasket and let the crowd of travellers have it both barrels.

"Clear off . . . let us bury my grandfather . . . please show some respect . . . go about your own business." Every phrase she screamed at them was like a blow and they gradually moved back.

Graham happened to know one of the travellers as he had had his drive tarmac'd a week or two ago. John saw his chance and got in close to someone he felt was a ringleader and said, "Look I'd appreciate it if you would give us some space to bury the old man. This is the funeral he wanted."

The guy was so nonplussed he agreed. "We'll, if that's what the old man wanted then let it be so, come away you little fockers." He told everyone to move away and John's assumption had been right, he was a ringleader. The inquisitive children were the hardest to move off but they did eventually move away with the mud clawing at their patent leather shoes.

The reason all these travellers were there was to bury a child, a child whose coffin and floral arrangements were as gaudy as its mourners' clothes. We had other matters to crystallise our attention.

Ann had brought a hostess trolley with her to help move the box to the graveside. She was all class. We, the self-designated pallbearers, especially the ones who hadn't carried the cardboard box yet, ignored the hostess trolley and, with the wooden plank giving strength, finally gave the skewed cardboard coffin a little dignity as it was lifted shoulder high. The smell from the box was overpowering and will never leave my nostrils, or anyone else'sfor that matter.

We carried the box easily to the hole. It was incredibly light. At least we didn't have to dig the hole. Although it wouldn't have been a surprise, after everything else had been so DIY. The men to fill the hole in were standing back respectfully waiting until we had finished our Heath-Robinson funeral. Apparently, this area of the graveyard was designated for eco-friendly funerals. My father was not the first weirdo to put his family through this disgraceful charade; not that I feel strongly about it.

There were two blocks of wood for the coffin and ropes to lower it. Guided by the gravediggers, who could see that we were new to DIY-burials and took pity on us, we were able to lower away.

Unfortunately, one end was heavier than the other was and started to descend faster than the other did and it became stuck on the side of the grave. At that point, the box started to open again. If my father had jumped out and started to do a jig I don't think anyone would have minded, because it was a whole lot more palatable than the alternative.

We all stopped lowering and everyone held their breath, if they weren't holding it already from the stench. Someone was able to jiggle the coffin free and it carried on its merry way. The collective sigh of relief was audible.

Because the entire event, other than hole digging and filling, was self-service there was no time limit and no real structure to the proceedings. With the coffin now safely in the ground, my sisters moved front and centre to speak. Ann kept apologising for the other traveller service not being finished, but everyone had finished listening to her some time ago. It was my father's daughters' time.

Jackie and Lynn spoke of happier times of a man I hardly knew. They were seven and nine years older than I was and had got to know a younger man, a man who still apparently had dreams and laughter in his life. They spoke of him brushing their hair, always insisting the dinner table was fully laid for every meal, whistling the same tune as he came home from work and how he taught them a love of reading.

By the end of their words, we were all crying. The hideousness of the day forgotten, momentarily, for us all to grieve. My sisters threw a rose in from each of them; they had one for me too. This was an act of rebellion as my father had asked for no flowers. They were a rare splash of colour on a grey, grey day.

For all my uncharitable thoughts about him, I felt incredibly sad and alone at that moment. And, to fend off my sobs, I thought positively.

Here was a man who had faced the fury of Nazi Germany as a 'Leading Torpedo Operator' on a high-speed Royal Navy Torpedo Boat during World War two. He had lied about his age to fight for his country. Here was a man who had dragged dead and badly wounded people from the sea. Here was a man who had struck his superior officer rather than compromise his principles. Here was a man, like most of us, who didn't want to face death wracked by pain or, as many see it, dehumanised by the curative process. Here was a man who felt he could not fight anymore, even to see one more dawn. Here was my father.

The travellers were starting to circle again and checking out the grave so we made off to the hotel where we would all have lunch together. No one could get their cars out of the cemetery because of the inconsiderate way the travellers had parked. We ignored it and decided to come back later. We were troubled enough by the events of the day so far, we didn't need any more traumas. No one was speaking.

Ann decided that as no one was listening to her she would remonstrate with the travellers. She yelled at them to move. A woman dressed in a pink fur coat with make-up reminiscent of a scary clown said, "We're the f**king Ravens of Harrow and we don't move for no one, so on your way."

There must have been five hundred travellers at their funeral all ridiculously dressed to our eyes, probably not to theirs. They had been banned from the hotel already so they wouldn't be following us in. Quite a few police were now around.

A buffet was laid out for us; all standard fare for a hotel, no one was in the mood for eating, however. The smell was still with us all. John, a confirmed carnivore, picked at a vegetarian dish. He later told me that if the day had been an episode of Only Fools and Horses, it would have been hilarious. If he didn't have the love for our family, and of course his wife, my cousin, I would have been embarrassed that he had had to go through it all.

I couldn't get over the selfishness of my father putting his extended family through such trauma. A funeral is not for the deceased; it is for the mourners to grieve. He was too self-centred to see that. He probably thought he was doing a good thing by having an ecologically friendly funeral, but he wasn't thinking of anyone but himself. It was a huge lesson for me.

We gathered around the bar still stunned by the occasion. We talked of all the drama, the travellers and so on when my sister Jackie, unwittingly said, "How awful, I think, had he seen it, Dad would have died."

Acknowledgements

Some of the names, timelines and other bits and bobs have been played around with somewhat, but in the most part They Saddle Dogs is true.

If you'll just indulge me a short while longer there are some people who need to be thanked. You can understand that, writing is a solitary thing but without others we'd be operating in a vacuum, which is exactly how my head sometimes feels when I'm writing.

My wife Virginia supported me, harangued me and disagreed with me. This book would not exist without her. She is now, and always will be, my best friend, my lover and my lightning rod. My children have suffered somewhat in the writing of this book. I'm hoping Virginia has told them I am not completely mad. I hope I've told them that myself. Watching me laugh, cry and talk to myself on some nights will have to be cleansed from their brains in expensive therapy sessions later on. Hopefully I'll sell enough books to pay for that.

Readers to be thanked, in no particular order other than the one my failing synapses chose, are; my sister Jackie Dowler, who also takes the position of chief cheerleader – a fine writer herself she has been a huge supporter of this book; Professor Andrew Madigan; Phil and Jancy Garrison; Edmund 'Eddie' O'Sullivan; Gina and John McNicholas. Not forgetting my friend Eudore Chand who could proof a page from 100 metres. I hope I haven't forgotten anyone.

The very nice people at Jerboa Books please take a bow. Without their belief in this book you'd probably be reading some revolting self-help book or another Michael Palin thingy by now, who knows? Isobel, Jane and their hardworking team deserve a big thank you.

We are a reflection of everything and everyone who has shaped us over the years, because of that, I would like to mention Andrea Finter, an exceptional friend and the one who put me on the path to writing. I am in her debt. Rest in peace, Andi, you left us too soon. Other extraneous thanks must go to The Cokers of Melbourne, Nick and Lisa Longden, Helen and Sam, Tim Elliott and Mark Fahy. I gladly include my childhood friends Les Hurlock and Paul 'Dolly' Dollard who have always 'had my back' through life. I am embarrassed at the wealth of friendship attained and freely admit that distance, death or spinelessness won't dim the keenness of its edge.

My whole extended family on both sides of the Atlantic, the Lockmans and the Hunts have been very supportive of my efforts to become 'a writer'. Thank you, I hope I have honoured your belief in me.

The last thing I need to do is thank my travelling companion for this truly amazing journey, chief dog saddler and fellow lunatic, Chris Osborne. Thank you for losing your religion with me, going with the flow and just being you. One day Oz-bob-whey will be free!

To you the reader of this, my first book, thank you and I'd love to hear your feedback on *They Saddle Dogs* - please feel free to email me at lockmanhunt@gmail.com.

Greg Hunt

Photograph by: Melanie Castellanos Contrast Professionals Dubai Tel: +971 4 2626292

A weekly columnist for the United Arab Emirates' national newspaper 7 Days, Travel Editor and business pundit for the Dubai Eye radio station and travel and business writer for too many publications to list, Greg was also the founder and former Group Editor of the MONEYworks group of magazines. Living with his wife, Virginia, and two children, Savannah and Gabriel, in Dubai, **They Saddle Dogs** is Greg Hunt's first book.

"The book THEY SADDLE DOGS *is a moving account of a journey of discovery in the Middle East and how the author's quest for help for his dying father led to a new understanding of what binds and divides."*

Eddie O'Sullivan
Editorial Director,
MEED (Middle East Economic Digest)